Lab Manual and Workbook for
PHYSICAL ANTHROPOLOGY

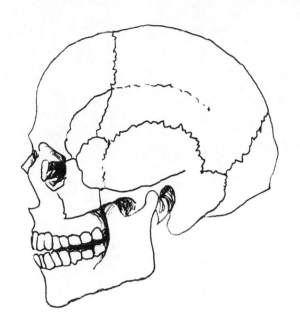

Lab Manual and Workbook for
PHYSICAL ANTHROPOLOGY

Diane L. France

Arthur D. Horn

Department of Anthropology,
Colorado State University, Fort Collins

WEST PUBLISHING COMPANY
St. Paul   New York   Los Angeles   San Francisco

Contents

Preface

This book is intended to be useful in two distinct situations. First, it contains many exercises in each chapter to be completed in laboratories with collections of human and nonhuman osteology and fossil hominoid casts. However, because many colleges and universities have no such collections, the book contains extensive photographs and drawings intended to some extent to take the place of those teaching aids. In this way, this book can also be used as a workbook and study aid in courses with no laboratory. To this end, and because this is intended to be a book for students with little or no prior training in physical anthropology, many study hints are scattered through each chapter.

Some chapters are greatly expanded compared to most textbooks or laboratory manuals now available. For instance, the chapter concerning human osteology is presented with numerous photographs of individual bones, with hints for recognizing entire or even somewhat fragmentary bones. Forensic anthropology, an applied aspect of physical anthropology which is becoming very important in the law enforcement fields, is not adequately covered in other laboratory notebooks or workbooks. Current techniques in personal identification of skeletal material are presented here, including the most recent techniques in age, sex, and race determination. The chapter in genetics is also quite long, both because the subject is important to the understanding of evolutionary theories, and because the student is taken step-by-step through genetics problems. Students are offered study hints and many exercises at each level of genetics, in an effort to eliminate confusion and to show that genetics is interesting and applicable to everyday life.

The sections in human evolution are unique in that the student is not only taught the current theories, but is encouraged to learn enough about the fossils and evolutionary theory to come up with potentially new evolutionary scenarios. In this way, this is an exploration of physical anthropology, not simply memorization of the facts and current theories. Chapters in very early primate evolution (Paleocene and Eocene epochs) are included, not only because they are important subjects of study in themselves, but also because they provide very important information for interpreting later fossils. The coverage of Miocene hominoid evolution is more complete than in most other texts and laboratory books as it is probably the epoch during which the human and great ape evolutionary lines diverged. Because we want the student to explore the possible theories, we have included information about methods (including current biochemical techniques) of study.

Physical anthropology is a wonderful and varied field of study.   In addition to the subjects covered in this book, physical anthropologists are also interested in hair analysis, dermatoglyphics, terrestrial and acquatic tissue decomposition rates, nutrition, human growth rates, studies in primate dentition, and many, many others, all of which cannot possibly be adequately covered in a single publication. We hope that the baseline knowledge which will be gained by the use of the this book will lead the students to explore some of these other areas.

F. Lynn Kilgore,   Alice M. Brues, Linda Couch, Calvin H. Jennings, and J.M. Suchey deserve special thanks for their constructive comments on this book. We also thank the following for their generous donations of drawings and photographs (listed in alphabetical order):   R.F. Kay, E. Mayr, D. Pilbeam, J.M. Suchey, R. Sussman, I. Tattersall, A. Walker, and D. Ubelaker.

Diane L. France
Arthur D. Horn

CREDITS

CHAPTER 1:   1 D. France. 2 A. Blackstone. 3-30 D. France
CHAPTER 2:   1-3 Jayne Bellavia. 4 D. Ubelaker, from Human Skeletal Remains:
Excavation, Analysis, Interpretation. Washington: Taraxacum Press. 5, 6 D.
France. 7 A. Blackstone. 8, 9 M. Burch, based on Katz, D., and J. M. Suchey,
"Age Determination of the Male Os Pubis," Am. J. Phys. Anthropology, 1986,
69:427-435. 10-21 D. France.
CHAPTER 3:   1-8 D. France.
CHAPTER 4:   1-12 D. France.
CHAPTER 5:   1 redrawn with permission from E. Mayr, from "Biological Classifi-
cation: Toward a Synthesis of Opposing Methodologies." Science, 214:510-516.
CHAPTER 6:   1-3 D. France. 4 Jayne Bellavia. 5-8 D. France.
CHAPTER 7: 1 A. Blackstone. 2 D. France, Carolina Biological Supply arti-
culated skeleton. 3 A. Blackstone with permission, from Napier, J.R. and A.C.
Walker, "Vertical Clinging and Leaping: A Newly-Recognized Category of Locomo-
tor Behavior of Primates," Folia Primat., 1967, 6:204-219. 4, 5 A. Horn. 6 A.
Blackstone. 7 D. France, San Diego Zoo. 8 D. France. 9 D. France, Carolina
Biological Supply articulated skeleton. 10 D. France. 11 A. Blackstone. 12 D.
France. 13, 14 D. France, Carolina Biological Supply articulated skeleton. 15
D. France. 16 D. France, Carolina Biological Supply articulated skeleton.
CHAPTER 8: No credits
CHAPTER 9:   1 courtesy of I. Tattersall, from Man's Ancestors: An Introduction
to Primate an Human Evolution, Levittown, New York: Transatlantic, 1970. 2
Robert Frank, from Jolly, C.J. and F. Plog, Physical Anthropology and Archaeo-
logy (3rd Ed.), from Random House, A. A. Knopf, Inc., New York. 3 Biruta
Akebergs after W.K. Gregory, from Jolly, C.J. and F. Plog, Physical Anthropo-
logy and Archaeology (3rd Ed.), from Random House, A. A. Knopf, Inc., New
York. 4 Biruta Akerbergs, from Jolly, C.J. and F. Plog, Physical Anthropology
and Archaeology (3rd Ed.), from Random House, A. A. Knopf, Inc., New York.
CHAPTER 10: 1 from Nelson, H. and R. Jurmain, Introduction to Physical Anthro-
pology (3rd Ed.), St. Paul: West Publishing Co., 1985. 2, 3 from Fleagle,
J.C., and R.F. Kay, "New Interpretations of the Phyletic Position of Oligocene
Hominoids." In: New Interpretations of Apes and Human Ancestry, R. Ciochon and
R. Corruccini (eds.). New York: Plenum Press. 4 D. France.
CHAPTER 11: 3 A. Blackstone 4 with permission, from Walker, A.C., and M.
Pickford, "New Postcranial Fossils of Proconsul africanus and Proconsul nyan-
zae." In: New Interpretations of Ape and Human Ancestry, R. Ciochon and R.
Corruccini (eds.), 1983, New York: Plenum Press. 5 courtesy of David Pilbeam.
6,7 D. France. 8, 9, 10 D. France, of Harvard casts. 11 D. France. 12 D.
France, of Harvard casts.
CHAPTER 12: 1,2 R.M. Matter, from Larsen, C.S., and R.M. Matter, Human Ori-
gins: the Fossil Record. Prospect Heights Illinois: Waveland Press, Inc.,
1985. 3 D. France. 4 D. France with permission, from R. Susman, from Susman,
R.L., J.T. Stern, Jr., and W.L. Jungers, "Arboreality and Bipedality in the
Hadar Hominids," Folia Primat., 1984, 43:113-156. 5 Alun Hughes, courtesy of
Professor P.V. Tobias, University of the Witwatersrand. 6 D. France, of cast.
7 R.M. Matter, from Larsen, C.S., and R.M. Matter, Human Origins: the Fossil
Record. Prospect Heights Illinois: Waveland Press, Inc., 1985. 8-11 D. France,
of casts. 12 D. France. 13 A. Blackstone. 14-17 D. France, of casts. 18 D.
France. 19-21 D. France, of casts. 22 A. Blackstone. 23 D. France, of casts.
24 A. Blackstone. 25-28 D. France, of casts.

Chapter 1

Human Osteology

INTRODUCTION

During this laboratory period, you will learn the names of the bones and of the major landmarks of the human skeleton. This task requires some memorization, but a good foundation in this chapter is vital to the understanding of almost all of the exercises within this entire book.

Various hints to help in learning the bones are given throughout this section. Additional space, too, is provided for you to write your own observations and drawings for each bone.

SOME FEATURES OF BONE

<u>Feature (plural): definition</u>

Cavity (cavities):	an open area
Condyle (condyles):	a rounded process
Diaphysis (diaphyses):	the shaft of bone
Epiphysis (epiphyses):	a process of bone initially attached to another piece of bone by cartilage, and usually later consolidated with it by bone.
Foramen (foramina):	a hole or opening
Fossa (fossae):	a pit, depression or cavity
Meatus (meatuses):	a canal
Process (processes):	any marked eminence
Tubercle (tubercles):	a small projection or process
Tuberosity (tuberosities):	a large projection or process

1

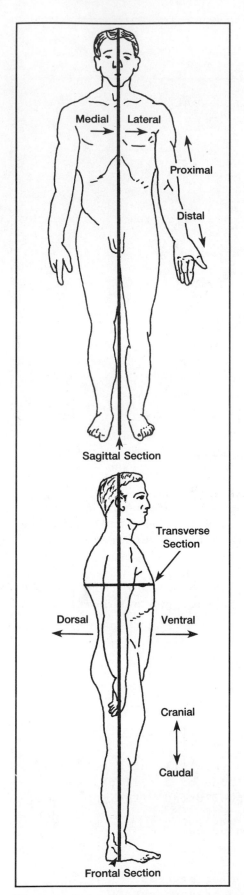

Sagittal Section

Frontal Section

Figure 1.1 Planes of the Body

Anterior:	in front (same as ventral)
Caudal:	towards the tail
Cranial:	towards the head
Distal:	farthest from the center of the body
Dorsal:	in back (same as posterior)
External:	outside of
Frontal:	in front
Inferior:	lower
Internal:	inside of
Lateral:	to the side, away from the midline
Medial:	toward the midline
Posterior:	behind, to the back (same as dorsal)
Proximal:	nearest the center of the body
Superficial:	near the surface
Superior:	above, top
Transverse:	crosswise
Ventral:	in front (same as anterior
Vertex:	top, highest point

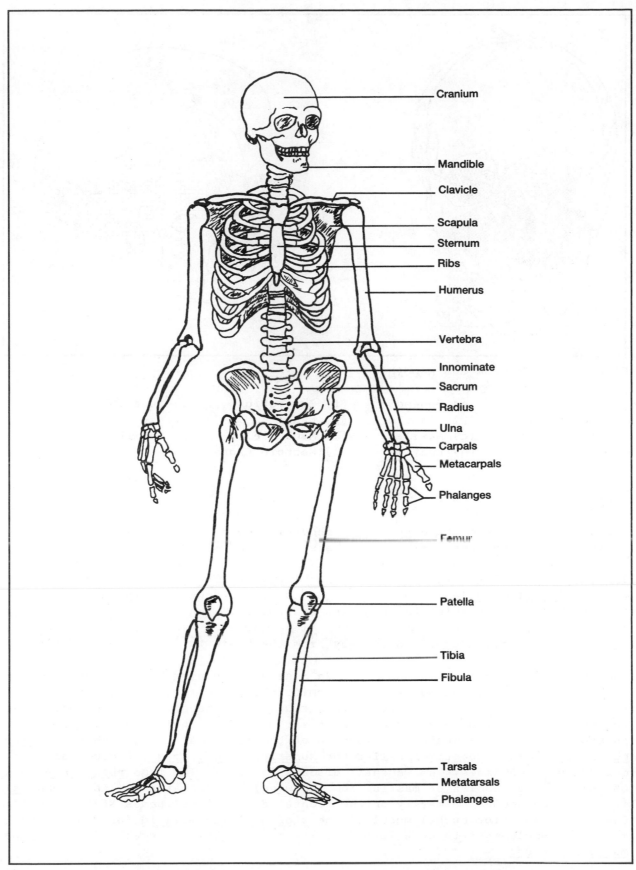

Figure 1.2 The Human Skeleton

3

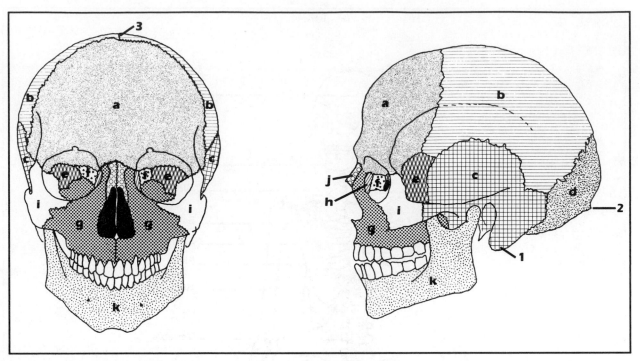

Figure 1.3 Cranium and Mandible

(a) Frontal   (e) Sphenoid*   (i) Zygomatic   (2) Superior Nuchal
(b) Parietal   (f) Ethmoid*   (j) Nasal   Line
(c) Temporal   (g) Maxilla   (k) Mandible   (3) Sagittal Suture
(d) Occipital   (h) Lacrimal*   (l) Mastoid Process

* get those straight.

Skull

The skull, consisting of cranium and mandible, is a very complex set of bones, serving to protect the brain, eyes, ears, nose and mouth.

The skull articulates with the first cervical vertebra (the atlas) by means of the occipital condyles (condyles = rounded projections, occipital refers to the cranial bone on which the condyles are found). The occipital condyles lie on the borders of the foramen magnum ("large hole"). The spinal cord passes through the foramen magnum on its way from the brain to the vertebral column.

The nuchal muscles (neck muscles) is a general term used to describe a group of muscles, including parts of the semispinalis capitis, the erector spinae longissimus, the splenius capitis, trapezius, and others. They are positioned on the back of the neck and have as their upper-most point of insertion a raised line on the posterior portion of the occipital bone, the superior nuchal line (also sometimes called the superior nuchal crest, especially in certain other animals, as we shall discuss later). The temporal muscle, one of the major muscles of mastication (chewing), originates on the temporal line, which occurs primarily on the frontal and parietal bones of the skull. One large anterior nuchal muscle, the sterno-cleido-mastoid (or just sterno-mastoid) muscle inserts on a large, downward-projecting process of bone, the mastoid process.

Locate the external auditory meatus (external opening of the ear), and the zygomatic arches (which form the bony prominence of the cheek, and can be felt just below and lateral to the eye). The zygomatic or malar bone is the bone of the cheek just below the eye.

On the frontal bone is often a raised, rounded area just above the eye orbits, called the supra-orbital torus ("raised area above the orbits", also called the brow ridges for obvious reasons).

The sagittal suture is a long straight suture ("tying together" the two parietal bones) running antero-posteriorly along the top of the cranium).

The coronal suture runs laterally from the top of the cranium, and ties together the frontal and two parietal bones.

Teeth

Caution: Teeth fall out of crania very easily--please be careful!

There are 20 deciduous (baby) teeth in children, and 32 permanent teeth in adults.

A dental formula is a count of the number and kinds of teeth an animal has, written in shorthand form. Only the teeth in one upper quadrant and often a lower quadrant are counted.

In each quadrant (upper left, upper right, lower left, lower right) there are two incisors (1 central, 1 lateral), one canine, two premolars (3rd, 4th*), and two or three molars (1st, 2nd, and 3rd or wisdom tooth). Hence the dental formula for a modern adult is 2:1:2:3, or 2:1:2:3

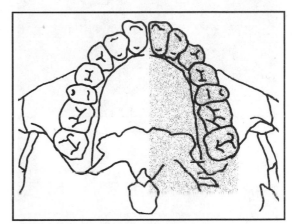

Figure 1.4 Tooth Row

    2:1:2:3 if upper and lower quadrants are counted.

In each quadrant of the child mouth there are two incisors (1 central, 1 lateral), one canine, two molars (1st, 2nd). The dental formula is therefore 2:1:0:2, or 2:1:0:2
    2:1:0:2 if upper and lower quadrants are counted.

*Primitive mammals have 4 premolars. In the course of evolution toward man, the first two premolars were lost, leaving the third and fourth.

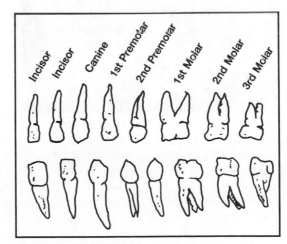

Figure 1.5 Teeth

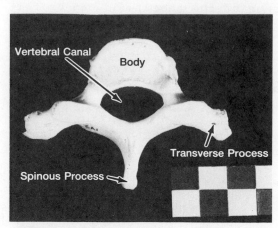

Figure 1.6 Typical Vertebra
Posterior is at bottom,
Anterior is at top

Vertebrae

The vertebral column is divided into 5 sections: cervical (7 in number), thoracic (12), lumbar (5), sacral (4-6), and coccygeal (3-5). The bodies of the cervical, thoracic, and lumbar vertebrae increase in size from the head toward the feet. The numbers of each type of vertebra may vary slightly from the number given. Note Figure 1.6 for features common to all vertebrae.

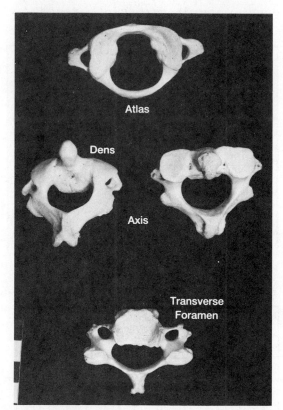

Figure 1.7 Cervical Vertebra
Atlas (top), Axis (middle),
Common Cervical Vertebra
(bottom)

Cervical Vertebrae

The first cervical vertebra, the atlas (it holds the "world", that is, cranium, on its shoulders) has no body. Its body has been "given" to the second cervical vertebra, the axis, to form the dens (or "tooth", as it looks like a tooth). The atlas (and hence the cranium) rotates around this dens.

The cervical vertebrae are the smallest weight-supporting vertebrae. The coccygeal vertebrae are smaller, but they support no weight. The cervicals are also recognizable in that they are the only vertebrae in which there is a foramen in the transverse process.

6

Thoracic vertebrae are easy to recognize, as they have facets for the articulation of the ribs. The articular processes (for the articulation of one vertebra onto another) are vertical and flat (except for the 12th, which has a lumbar vertebra-type process on the inferior surface).

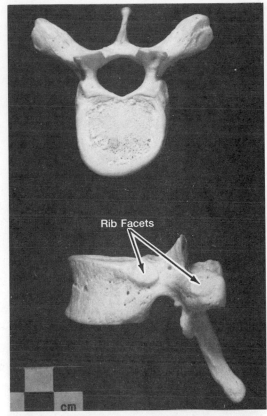

Rib Facets

Figure 1.8 Thoracic Vertebra

Lumbar vertebrae are the largest (they carry the most weight) of the movable vertebrae. The processes for articulation with the other vertebrae are vertical and curved, to interlock with each other, giving a much stronger intervertebral articulation. Lumbar vertebrae have no rib facets.

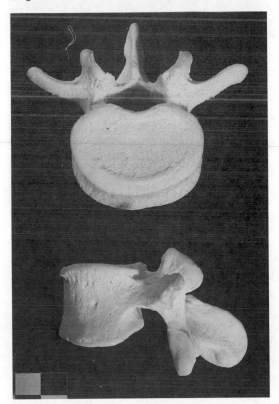

Figure 1.9 Lumbar Vertebra

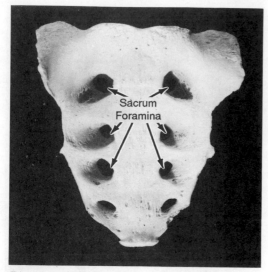

Figure 1.10   Sacrum,
    Anterior View

Sacral vertebrae, usually 5 but sometimes 4 or 6 in number, are fused in the adult to form a single bone, the sacrum. The weight of the upper body in man is passed to the innominate bones and femora through the sacrum, so this bone must be strong and stable.

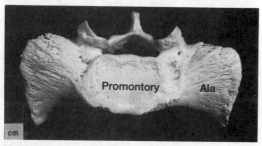

Figure 1.11   Sacrum,
    Superior View

The sides of the upper sacral vertebrae are flared into wings, or alae, to form a large surface which articulates with the ilium.

Figure 1.12   Coccygeal
    Vertebra, Anterior View

Coccygeal vertebrae give no support to the vertebral column, but are the site of origin of a few muscles and ligaments. Note: occasionally loose lower coccygeal vertebrae are confused with the body of the unfused hyoid bone.

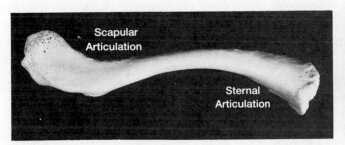

Figure 1.13 Clavicle
Superior View

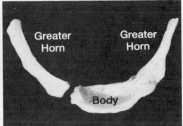

Figure 1.14 Hyoid
Bone

The <u>clavicle</u>: is a long bone which maintains a constant distance between the scapula and sternum, and thereby adds strength to the shoulder girdle. The medial end is rounded for articulation with the sternum, the lateral end is flattened (and roughened inferiorally) for articulation with the scapula.

The <u>hyoid bone</u> is a very small bone which does not articulate directly with any other bone, but is suspended below the mandible by many muscles acting on the tongue, pharynx, and neck. It is very often broken in strangulation victims.

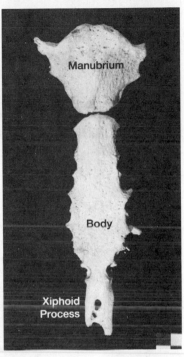

Figure 1.15 Sternum
Anterior View

The <u>sternum</u> is composed of three segments, and is similar to a broadsword.

1. <u>Manubrium</u> ("handle"), has articulation facets for clavicle and rib.
2. <u>Body</u> ("blade"), has articulation facets for ribs.
3. <u>Xiphoid process</u> ("tip"), often a cartilaginous tab, becoming bony in later years.

The three segments of this bone are sometimes separate, but most often fused in adults.

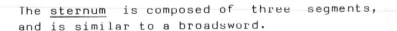

9

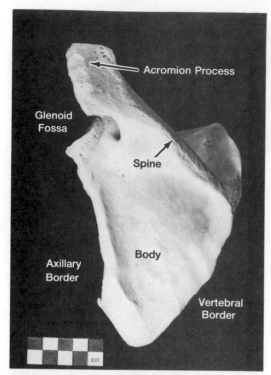

Figure 1.16 Scapula,
Dorsal Surface

The <u>scapula</u> is a triangular flat bone which rests on the upper back. It has two major projections on the proximal lateral angle: the <u>coracoid process</u> and the <u>acromion process</u> which are both points of origin of muscles of the upper back and arm. The acromion process articulates with the clavicle, and is one of the points used by a tailor to calculate sleeve length.

The body and spine of the scapula support many of the muscles of the back.

The <u>glenoid fossa</u> is the point of articulation of the head of the humerus.

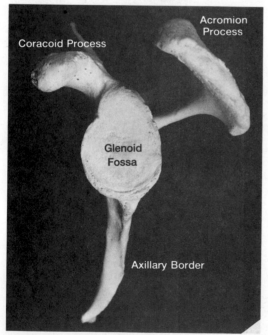

Figure 1.17 Scapula,
Glenoid Fossa

The _humerus_ is the lar-
gest bone of the arm.
It articulates with the
scapula at the glenoid
fossa at the proximal
end, and with the radius
and ulna at the distal
end.

The _ulna_ is the medial
bone of the forearm, and
articulates proximally
with the humerus, and
laterally with the ra-
dius. The _semilunar_
notch at the proximal
end forms a "U" (which
should help you remember
"ulna").

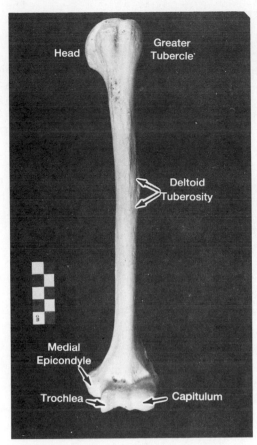

Figure 1.18   Humerus

The _radius_ is the lateral bone of the forearm,
and "follows" the thumb
in the movements of the
forearm in _pronation_ and
supination (pronation:
rotation of the hand and
forearm so that the palm
faces downward or toward
the body; supination is
the rotation of the hand
and forearm back to the
anatomical position of
palms up). The radius
crosses over the ulna in
pronation. The proximal
surface is rounded for
articulation with the
capitular surface of the
humerus, so think of the
"radius of a circle"
when remembering the
radius.

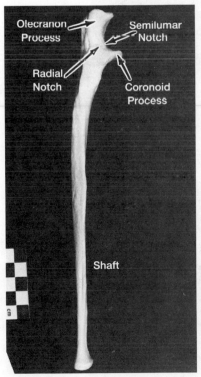

Figure 1.19   Ulna

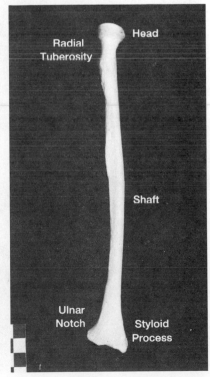

Figure 1.20   Radius

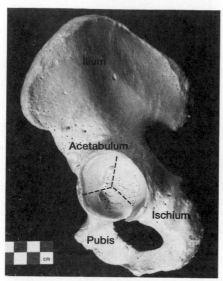

Figure 1.21 Innominate
Lateral View

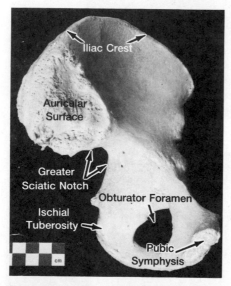

Figure 1.22 Innominate
Medial View

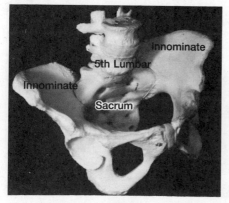

Figure 1.23 Articulated
Pelvic Girdle

The _innominata_ are the two large bones of the pelvis, which join with the sacrum to form the pelvic girdle.

Although the innominate is one unit in the adult, it actually consists of three separate bones, all coming together in the _acetabulum_.

1. _Ilium_: upper portion
The _iliac crest_ is the most superior edge of the ilium, and can be felt through the skin. Posteriorly, the _greater sciatic notch_ is a deep incurve.

2. _Ischium_: the most posterior bone of the innominate. The _ischial tuberosity_ supports the body in the sitting position.

3. _Pubis_: the most anterior portion. It articulates with the pubic bone from the opposite side at the _pubic symphysis_ to form the anterior wall of the pelvis.

The femur is the largest and longest bone in the human body (not so of all other animals, as we shall see later). The head of the femur articulates proximally with the acetabulum, and the condyles articulate with the condyles of the tibia distally.

The head of the femur is a more complete ball than the head of the humerus. The head exhibits a pit, the fovea capitis, in the center, at which the very strong ligamentum teres connects the femur to the acetabulum and carries blood to the femur. The femur is much more difficult to dislocate than the head of the humerus in the living.

The tibia, the largest bone of the lower leg, has a tibial tuberosity and a sharp shin, both of which can be palpated in the living. The medial malleolus of the distal tibia forms the medial projection of the ankle felt in the living.

The fibula is, with the tibia, the analog of the radius and ulna of the arm, though the leg has lost most of the pronation - supination function. The lateral malleolus of the distal fibula forms the lateral projection of the ankle felt in the living.

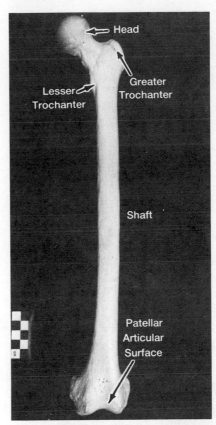

Figure 1.24 Femur

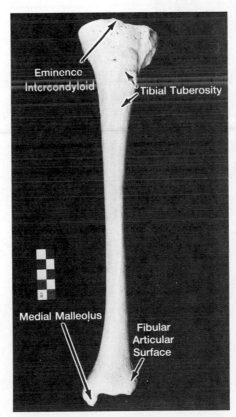

Figure 1.25 Tibia

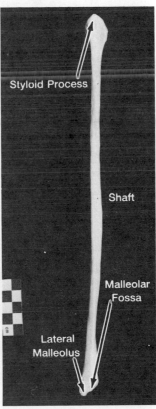

Figure 1.26 Fibula

13

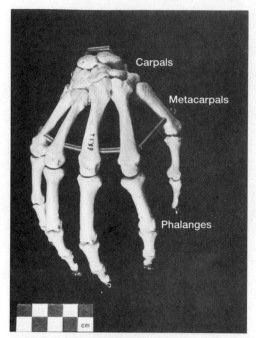

Figure 1.27 Right Hand

The <u>wrist</u> and <u>hand</u> consist of many different kinds of bones.

The <u>carpals</u> are the eight wrist bones, the <u>navicular</u> (or <u>scaphoid</u>), <u>lunate</u>, <u>triquetral</u>, <u>pisiform</u>, <u>greater multangular</u> (or <u>trapezium</u>), <u>lesser multangular</u> (or <u>trapezoid</u>), <u>capitate</u> and <u>hamate</u>.

The <u>metacarpals</u> make up the body of the living hand between the wrist and the projection of the fingers. They are simply numbered 1 through 5.

The <u>phalanges</u> are the bones of the fingers. The thumb has two (proximal and distal), all other fingers have three each (proximal, middle, and distal).

Ankle and Foot:

The <u>tarsals</u> are the seven bones which make up the ankle: the <u>calcaneus</u>, <u>talus</u>, <u>navicular</u>, <u>first</u> <u>cuneiform</u>, <u>second</u> <u>cuneiform</u>, <u>third</u> <u>cuneiform</u>, and <u>cuboid</u>.

The <u>metatarsals</u> are analogous to the metacarpals of the hand, and make up the body of the foot. Again, they are simply numbered 1 through 5.

The <u>phalanges</u> of the foot are again analogous to the phalanges of the hand.

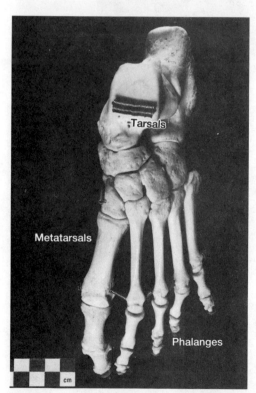

Figure 1.28 Left Foot

The _patella_ is the knee-cap, which rests just anterior to the distal femur. The patella points distally, and is rounded proximally.

Figure 1.29 Patella

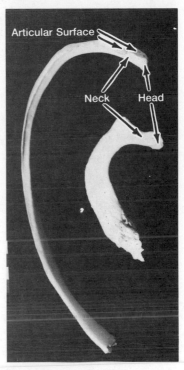

The _ribs_ are in general easy to recognize. The superior surface is rounded, the inferior surface is rather sharp, and the rib is flat medio-laterally. The region around the head articulates with the lateral vertebral body and transverse process.

The first rib, however, is flat cranio-caudally, and is very much shorter than the other ribs.

The first seven ribs are _true_ ribs, in that they articulate with the sternum at the readily observable _costal_ (rib) notches.

Figure 1.30 Ribs
Inferior View
Standard Rib (left)
1st Rib (right)

The 8th, 9th and 10 ribs are _false_ ribs in that they don't articulate directly with the sternum, but to a common cartilage which itself articulates with the distal sternum.

The 11th and 12th ribs are _floating_ ribs, so-called because they have no connection at all to the sternum.

Exercises

1.   Short Answer

      Raised, rounded areas just above the eye orbits are the: *supra-orbital torus (brow-ridges)*

      The suture which joins the two parietal bones is the: *sagittal suture*

      The skull articulates with the vertebra by means of: *the dens – the body of the 1st cervical vertibrae (atlas) given to the 2nd cervical vertibrae; axis*

      The point on the scapula which articulates with the humerus: ~~vs. supination, the att~~ *acromium process*

      Rotation of the hand and forearm so that the palm faces downward: *pronation vs. supination : the anatomical position*

      The medial bone of the forearm (in the anatomical position): *ulna (semilunar notch: U-shape)*

2.   What is the definition of a dental formula?
      Count of number & kinds of teeth in upper & or lower quadrant

3.   What is the dental formula of an adult human? *2:1:2:3*
                                            Child : 2:1:0:2

4.   What morphological features make a cervical vertebra unlike other vertebrae? *foramen in the transverse process*

5.   What morphological features make a thoracic vertebra distinct from other vertebrae? *Rib facets for articulation w the ribs*

6.   What are the three segments of a sternum? *① Manubrium ② Body ③ Xiphoid process (cart. in children)*

7.   What are the three bones of each innominate? *① Ilium ② Ischium ③ pubis*

8.   How is the head of the humerus different from the head of the femur? *– more of a ball than head of humerus – has a pit – fovea capitis – in centre for ligamentum teres for attachment to acetabulum*

9.   What are the eight bones of the carpals? Of the tarsals?

10.   How is the first rib different from the other ribs?

Chapter 2

Forensic Anthropology

INTRODUCTION

Forensics is defined as the application of scientific methods to the law. Forensic anthropology is, therefore, the application of anthropological method to the law, and is usually used in determining the identity of a skeleton or partial skeleton. The judgment as to identity begins with the determination of age, sex, race, stature, abnormalities and/or pathologies, and idiosyncrasies. In your studies so far, you have seen enough of the human skeleton to know what one looks like; now let's be more specific.

Determination of Sex

In general, males are bigger than females: the bones are larger and the areas devoted to muscle attachment are larger and more rugged, just as in other primate species, most notably the gorillas and orang-utans. This is sexual dimorphism. However, in order to utilize this size difference in sex determination, the researcher must be able to identify the population from which the skeleton was taken, as whole populations differ in skeletal size. For example, Asian Indians are much smaller than Australian Aborigines. A male Asian Indian skeleton placed alongside a male (or probably even a female) Australian Aborigine skeleton would, if judged on the basis of size, be misclassified as a female. A study performed on humeri of Arikara vs. Pueblo North American Indian groups) misclassified almost 70% of the male Pueblo humeri on the basis of size alone, indicating that relatively great general size differences between these two populations could confuse sex differences (France, 1983).

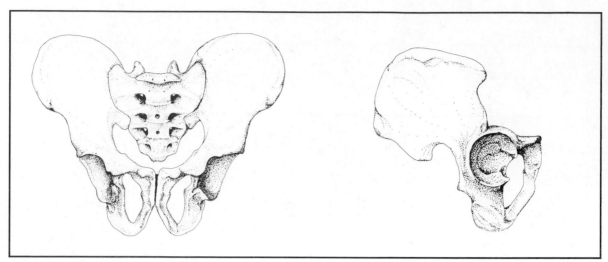

Figure 2.1   Male Pelvic Girdle

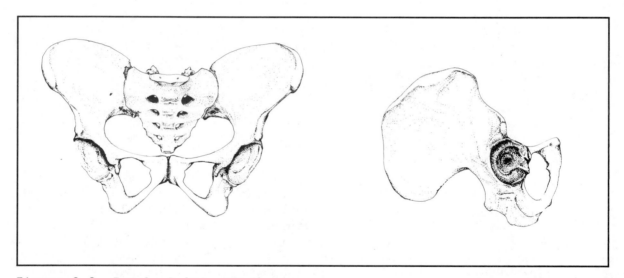

Figure 2.2   Female Pelvic Girdle

Pelvic Girdle	Typical Male	Typical Female
Subpubic Angle	Less than 90 degrees	More than 90 degrees
Pubic Shape	Triangular	Rectangular
Subpubic Angle Shape (see also Phenice 1969)	Convex ⌒	Concave ⌣
Greater Sciatic Notch	Less than 68 degrees	More than 68 degrees
Sacrum	Smaller and more curved	Larger and straighter

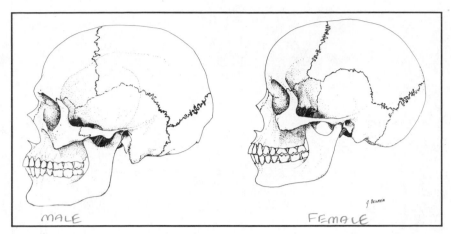

Figure 2.3   Cranium and Mandible: Male (left), Female (right)

Cranium	Typical Male	Typical Female
Muscle Attachment Areas mastoid process, etc.	More pronounced	Less pronounced
Supraorbital Torus (brow ridges)	More pronounced	Less pronounced
Frontal Bone	Slanting	Globular
Supraorbital Rim (in eye orbit)	Rounded	Sharp
Palate	Deep	Shallow

Other Areas		
Suprascapular Notch on Scapula	Often Present	Often Absent
Femur: Angle of Neck to Shaft	Smaller Angle	Greater Angle

The most reliable skeletal area for the determination of sex is, as one might guess, the pelvic girdle. This is the one area of the body for which a sexual difference has clear natural selection ramifications, for if the birth canal is not large enough in females for the newborn (or, new-about-to-be-born) to pass, the infant will die (and perhaps the mother as well), and her genes will not be passed on to the next generation. When the entire skeleton is avail- able for inspection, the pelvic area should be the most important for sex determination, but do not ignore the other areas of the skeleton: the more information you can gather, the better.

The previous standards are for skeletons past adolescence; pre-adolescent sexing techniques are not as yet widely used.

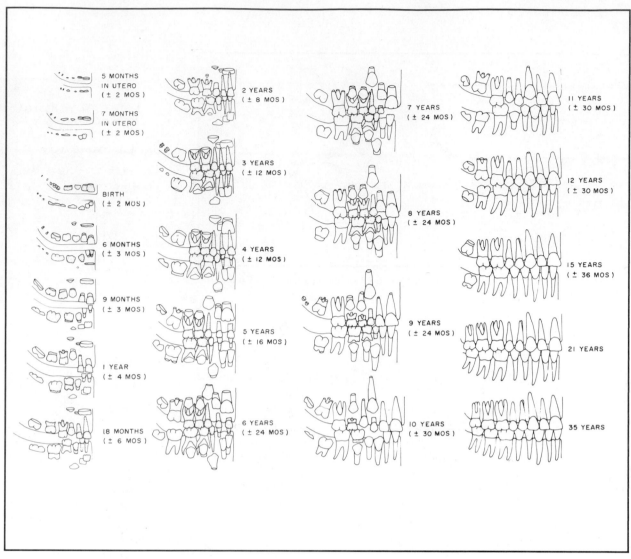

Figure 2.4   Dental Eruption Chart (Courtesy D. Ubelaker)

DETERMINATION OF AGE

Several methods are commonly employed in the determination of the physiological age of a skeleton.   Researchers hope that the physiological age will
give an accurate estimate of chronological age, but environmental, nutri-
tional, and disease stresses will often cause changes in the skeleton which
will mask the true age of the individual.

Dental Eruption (Figure 2.4)

The determination of the ages at which the deciduous and permanent dentition
erupts is useful in identifying age to approximately 15 years.   The third
molar (wisdom tooth) erupts after this time, but is so variable in age of
eruption (if it erupts, as many never do), that is not a very reliable age
indicator.

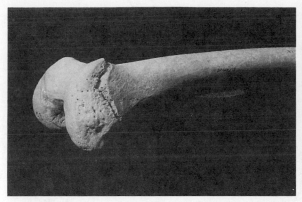 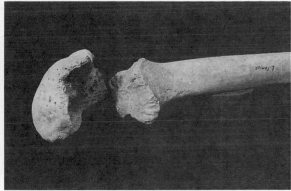

Figure 2.5 Unfused
Distal Femur

Figure 2.6 Unfused
Distal Femur

Bone Growth

Postcranial bones are formed initially in cartilage; that is, a cartilage model precedes actual formation of bone. At different times during growth, depending on the bone, osteoblasts (bone-forming cells) invade the cartilage to lay down bone. The so-called ossification centers are the points at which this initially occurs in each bone. The primary centers of growth (or diaphyses; singular = diaphysis) are responsible for most of the length of long bones. The secondary centers (or epiphyses; singular = epiphysis) are separated from the diaphyses by metaphyses (singular = metaphysis), which are thin layers of cartilage being overtaken by bone formation. The metaphysis is the actual site of bone growth. When the diaphysis meets the epiphysis, the metaphysis disappears, the ends of the bones fuse, and growth ceases. Because this occurs at different times in different bones, the age of an individual can be determined by which epiphyses have fused and which have not. In Figures 2.5 and 2.6 show an epiphysis and diaphysis which have not yet fused. Notice the characteristic undulating appearance of the unfused surfaces of bone.

Females age more quickly than males, so usually 1 to 2 years must be subtracted from the previous ages for female skeletons.

Ectocranial Suture Closure
⌐outside the cranium
At one time this method was used quite extensively, though with more research the dates of closure were found to vary widely, making the ageing unreliable. This technique may, according to Meindl and Lovejoy (1985) be enjoying a comeback, but as yet it is no longer widely used, and will not be emphasized in this book.

Endocranial (inside the cranium) suture closures are probably more reliable, but are often difficult to see and interpret.

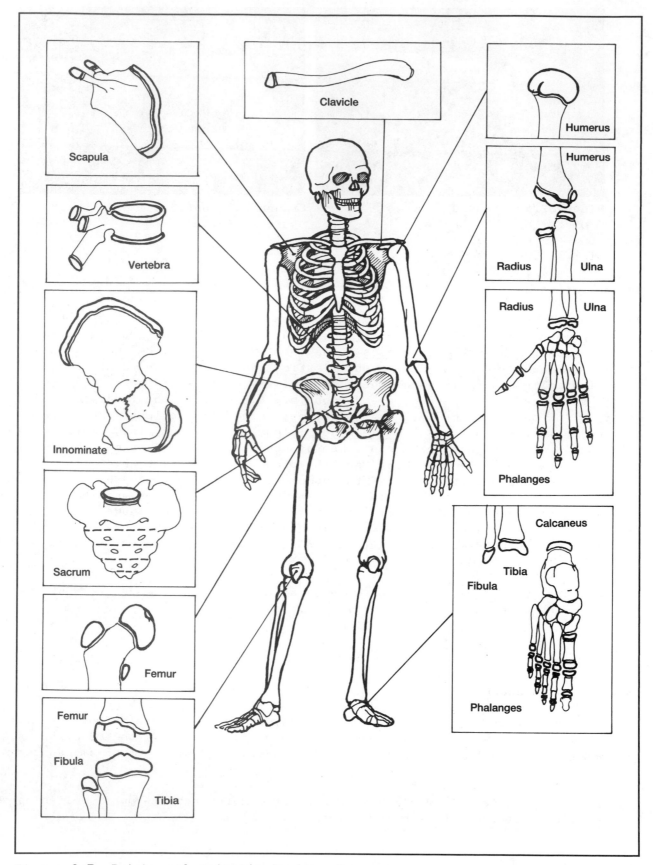

Figure 2.7 Epiphyseal Union in Various Bones

Skeletal Age: Epiphyseal Unions

Area of Body	Age		Age
Scapula		**Femur**	
Acromion Process	16 - 22	Head	14 - 19
Vertebral Margin	17 - 22	Gr. Trochanter	14 - 19
Inferior Angle	17 - 22	Le. Trochanter	14 - 19
Coracoid Process	15 - 18	Distal	16 - 20
Clavicle		**Tibia**	
Sternal End	23 - 28	Proximal	17 - 22
Acromial End	19 - 20	Distal	15 - 19
Humerus		**Fibula**	
Head	16 - 23	Proximal	16 - 20
Distal	12 - 16	Distal	14 - 20
Medial Epicondyle	14 - 19		
		Calcaneus	14 - 18
Radius			
Proximal	14 - 18	**Vertebrae**	
Distal	17 - 19	Epiphyseal Plates	19 - 25
Ulna		**Foot**	
Proximal	13 - 18	Metatarsals	14 - 18
Distal	17 - 20	Phalanges	14 - 18
Hand		**Basilar Suture**	20
Metacarpals	14 - 18	(cranium)	
Phalanges	14 - 18		
Pelvis			
Primary Elements	13 - 15		
Iliac Crest	18 - 23		
Ischial Tuberosity	16 - 23		
Sacrum			
Bodies and Vertebral "Rings", from caudal upwards	18 - 25		

These ages are approximation of completed union compiled from several sources (McKern and Stewart 1957, Bass 1987, and Krogman 1939).   For more complete information, consult these sources.   All ages are given for white males, subtract 1 to 2 years for female age determination.

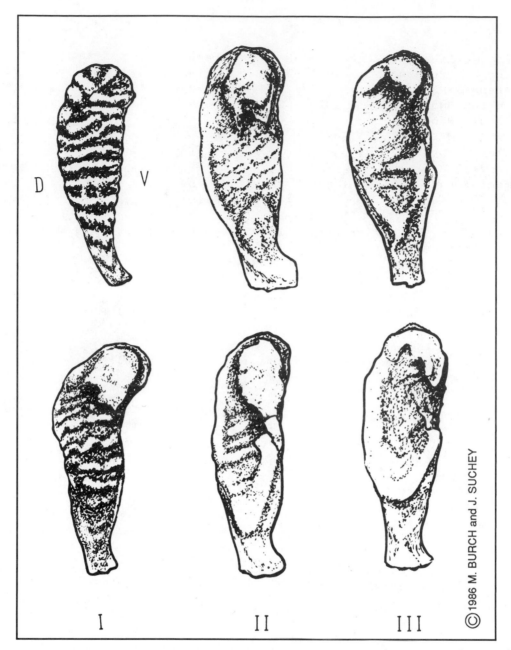

D   V

I   II   III

Figure 2.8 Suchey-Brooks Male Pubic Symphyseal Phases (I-III)
Left Side Illustrated, D=Dorsal, V=Ventral
Based on Katz and Suchey 1986: 427-435 (Courtesy J. Suchey).

forms the anterior
wall of the pelvis

Pubic Symphyseal Face: The pubic symphyseal face in the young is characterized
by an undulating surface, such as seen on a normal epiphysis, but undergoes
regular metamorphysis from age eighteen onwards.   Several researchers have
developed age determination techniques based on the changing morphology of the
symphyseal face.   The first technique was developed by T.W. Todd (1920, 1921)
utilizing dissection room cadavers.   McKern and Stewart (1957) developed a
technique using American males killed in the Korean War.   Both of the samples
from which these systems were derived have limitations in that the dissection
room sample used by Todd is based on individuals of uncertain age (Brooks
1985, 1986) and the Korean War Dead sample is predominantly young Caucasoid

26

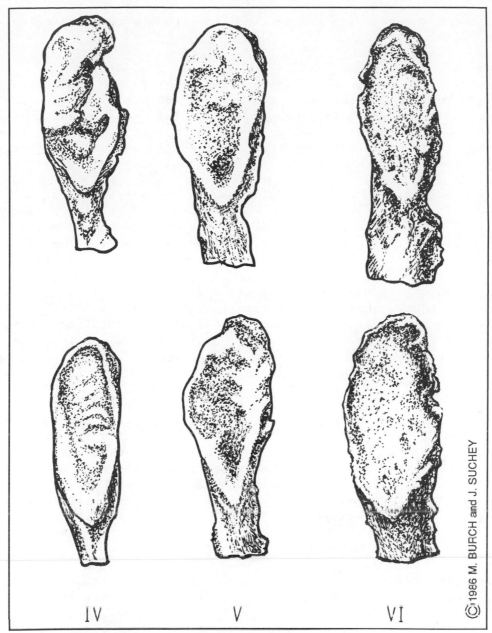

Figure 2.9: Suchey-Brooks Male Pubic Symphyseal Phases (IV - VI)
Based on Katz and Suchey 1986: 427-435 (Courtesy J. Suchey).

males, with few individuals over age 35.

Recently a system has been developed by J.M. Suchey, D. Katz and S.T. Brooks based on a large sample (n = 739) of males for whom legal documentation of age is provided by death certificates. This autopsy room sample should be more representative of the general population than past samples. The majority of the males were born throughout the United States and Mexico. This sample was taken at autopsy involving homicides, suicides, accidents, or unexpected natural deaths. This six phase system is illustrated in Figures 2.8 and 2.9.

Note: These six phases are not sequential; the age ranges overlap, although the means differ.

Phase <u>I</u> (mean = 18.9, S.D. = 2.3, 95% range = 15-23 years)
   Symphyseal face has a billowing surface (ridges and furrows) which extends to include the pubic tubercle. The horizontal ridges may be either well-marked or in process of obliteration. Dorsal plateau may be in beginning phases of formation; ventral border is not yet forming. A key to the recognition of this phase is the lack of delimitation of extremities (upper and lower). Ossific nodules may occur.

Phase <u>II</u> (mean = 24.7, S.D. = 4.3, 95% range = 19-35 years)
   Symphyseal face shows commencing delimitation of lower and/or upper extremities. Some bones still show ridge development. Dorsal margin is completed. Ventral border, upper and lower extremities, may be in process of delimitation through presence of developing ossific nodules.

Phase <u>III</u> (mean = 28.8, S.D. 5.9, 95% range = 22-43 years)
   Symphyseal face shows lower extremity and ventral rampart in process of completion. There is a continuation of fusing ossific nodules forming the upper extremity and ventral border. Symphyseal face is smooth or can continue to show distinct ridges. Absence of lipping of symphyseal margin; no bony ligamentous outgrowths.

Phase <u>IV</u> (mean = 36.8, S.D. = 9.6, 95% range = 23-59 years)
   Symphyseal face is generally finely grained although remnants of the old ridge and furrow system may still remain. Usually the oval outline is complete at this stage, but occasionally a hiatus can occur in ventral rim. Pubic tubercle is fully separated from the symphyseal face by definition of upper extremity. The symphyseal face may have a distinct rim. Commencing bony outgrowths on inferior half of symphysis pubis may occur. However, there is no marked lipping of symphyseal margin.

Phase <u>V</u> (mean = 51.0, S.D. = 13.6, 95% range = 28-78 years)
   Symphyseal face is completely rimmed with some slight depression of the face itself, relative to the rim. More pronounced "rimming" occurs on the dorsal margin, with moderate lipping on the ventral margin.

Phase <u>VI</u> (mean = 62.7, S.D. = 12.4, 95% range = 36-87 years)
   Symphyseal face shows ongoing depression as rim erodes. Ventral ligamentous attachments are marked. In many individuals the pubic tubercle appears as a separate bony knob. The face may be pitted or porous, giving an appearance of disfigurement with the ongoing process of erratic ossification.

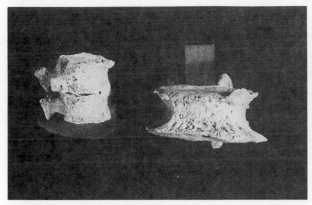

Figure 2.10 Degenerative Changes in the Vertebrae

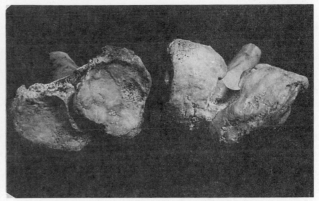

Figure 2.11 Degenerative Changes in the Femur and Tibia

Old Age

Basically, the developmental changes which characterize young skeletons give way to the degenerative changes of old age. Arthritis becomes more prevalent and pronounced, as does osteoporosis (increased porosity of the bone, particularly in post-menopausal women). These changes can give corroborative evidence to determinations of older age, but are not reliable by themselves, as injury and disease can mimic many of these changes in the skeleton.

DETERMINATION OF RACE

A controversy in anthropology exists today over whether or not "races" exist. In some ways it can be said that there is no such thing as a race; that sets of morphological traits cannot distinguish groups of individuals from all others in such a way as to be able to label all of the people in the world. Even skin color, the most noticeable of characteristics, cannot adequately categorize all individuals, for there are darkly-skinned Caucasoids and Mongoloids (disregarding the effects of tanning), and lightly-skinned Negroids.

Forensic anthropologists, however, would find it very difficult to ignore the morphological differences which can help to distinguish between peoples. When an anthropologist is asked to help in the identification of a parcel of bones, part of that identification must include a statement as to probable race, because race is included in the social identity of that person. This identification is often difficult, however, as most of the morphological characteristics we use to distinguish race follow a continuum; that is, one trait is more often, but not exclusively, associated with one race. For example, as is seen below, dolicocephaly is usually associated with Negroids, but individuals of other races may also show this trait (e.g. Northern Europeans). In fact, it can be said that there is more variation within races than between races. Also please note that the concept of racial purity is largely myth--we expect some admixture in most of the cases we study.

The races of the world have been divided in different ways in history, but many anthropologists today readily identify three basic groups: Mongoloids (including Japanese, Chinese, and North, Central, and South American Indians),

Negroids (including African and American Blacks, Australoids), and Caucasoids (including Europeans, and other people with European ancestry, Asian Indians, and some North African peoples). This is not by any means a complete classification scheme, nor is it the only classification scheme used by physical anthropologists today.

The chart below lists some of the differences we usually see in the skulls of the various races (most of the currently important differences used in the identification of race occurs in the skulls) (see also Brues 1977, Krogman 1962, Stewart 1979, and Bass 1987).

Feature	Negroid	Caucasoid	Mongoloids
Central Incisors (cross section) (Dahlberg 1951)	Blade	Rarely Shoveled	Shoveled
*Cranial Shape	Dolicocranic (long)	Mesocranic (medium)	Brachycranic (round)
Nasal Root (at root of nose)	Wide, Rounded	Narrow, Pinched	Medium, tented
**Nasal Aperture	Platyrrhiny (wide)	Leptorrhiny (narrow)	Mesorrhiny (medium)
Zygomatic Bone	Medium	Retreating	Projecting
External Auditory Meatus (ear opening)	Round	Round	Oval
Facial Shape	Prognathic (lower face projects forward)	Orthognathic (lower face non-projecting)	Medium

* The Cranial Shape is obtained from the Cranial Index, calculated from:

$$\frac{\text{Cranial Breadth}}{\text{Cranial Length}} \times 100$$

Up to 75 = Dolicocrany
75 - 79.9 = Mesocrany
80 - 84.9 = Brachycrany
85 and up = Hyperbrachycrany
(Bass 1987)

** The Nasal Aperture Shape is obtained from the Nasal Index:

$$\frac{\text{Nasal Breadth}}{\text{Nasal Height}} \times 100$$

up to 47.9 = Leptorrhiny
48 - 52.9 = Mesorrhiny
53 and up = Platyrrhiny
(Bass 1987)

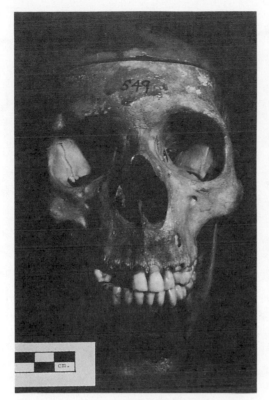

Figure 2.12 American Negroid

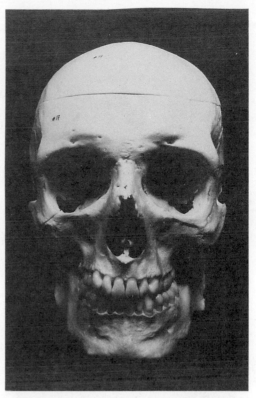

Figure 2.13 American Caucasoid

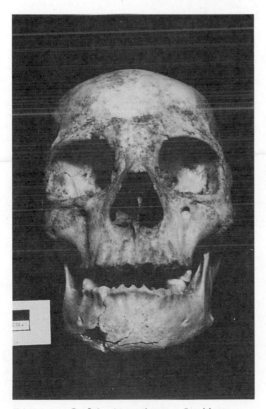

Figure 2.14 American Indian

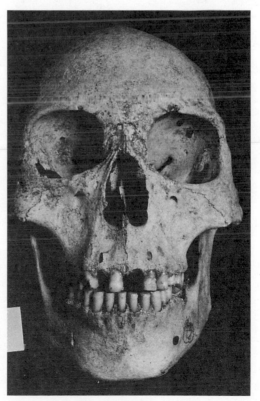

Figure 2.15 Eskimo

1. a. Is the bone in Figure 2.16 an adult
or sub-adult?
    b. How can you tell?
    c. What is the approximate age of this
individual?

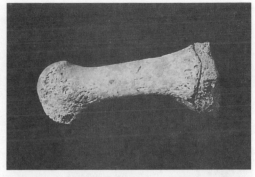

Figure 2.16 Foot Phalange

2. a. Is the bone in Figure 2.17 an adult
or sub-adult?
    b. How can you tell?
    c. What is the approximate age of this
individual?

Figure 2.17 Calcaneus

3.   Figure 2.18 shows a pubic symphyseal
face.
    a.   Using the Suchey-Brooks male aging
system, to what phase would you assign
this bone?
    b.   What is the approximate age of
this individual?

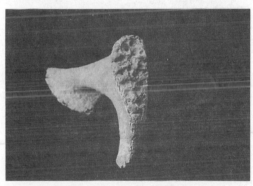

Figure 2.18 Pubic Symphysis

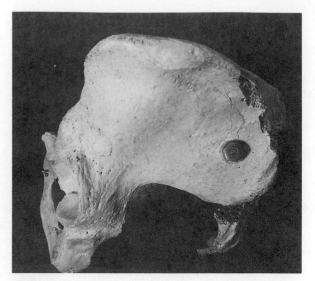

Figure 2.19 Innominate

4. What is the sex of the individual represented in Figure 2.19?
How can you tell?

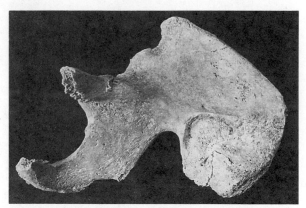

Figure 2.20 Innominate

5. What is the sex of the individual represented in Figure 2.20?
How can you tell?

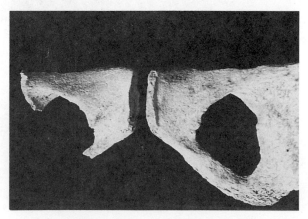

Figure 2.21 Pubic Bones
   at Symphysis

6. What is the sex of the individual represented in Figure 2.21?
How can you tell?

Chapter 3

Anthropometry

INTRODUCTION

Various measurements of the living body are useful to anthropologists, geneticists, physicians, and even to manufacturers of goods which fit on or around the body (clothing, car seats and seatbelts, for instance). There are an infinite number of measurements one can take on the human body, limited primarily by the practicality in finding easily discovered and described landmarks.

Many tools (often very expensive) are used in anthropometric measurements. These tools are shown in the measurement description photographs, and are additionally described and shown in Chapter 6.

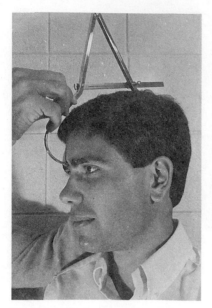 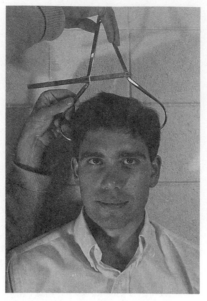 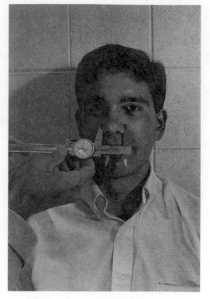

Figure 3.1 Head Length   Figure 3.2 Head Width   Figure 3.3 Width of
Nasal Alae

MEASUREMENT DESCRIPTIONS

A. The following are taken with spreading calipers:

    1. Head Length: taken from the sagittal line of the forehead, between the brow ridges to the maximum measurement in the sagittal line of the occipital region (Figure 3.1).

    2. Maximum Head Width: the maximum width of the head, usually just below and behind the ears (Figure 3.2).

B. The following are taken with sliding calipers.

    3. Width of Fleshy Alae of Nose: the maximum width of alae: do not apply distorting pressure (Figure 3.3).

    4. Length of Nose: from nasal root (or nasion: see Chapter 5 for definition) to tip of nose: no distorting pressure should be applied (Figure 3.4).

    5. Length of Middle Finger: of each hand. This should include only the combined lengths of the phalanges (do not include the metacarpal) (Figure 3.5).

C. The following are usually taken with the anthropometer rod, but cloth tape may be used.

    6. Standing Height: taken in stocking feet to the vertex of the head.

    7. Sitting Height: while the subject is sitting on a table, taken from the surface of the table to the vertex of the head (Figure 3.6).

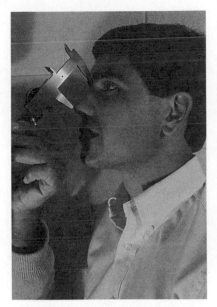

Figure 3.4 Nose Width

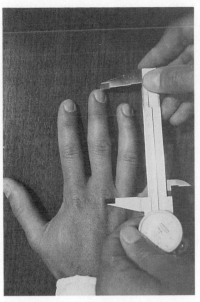

Figure 3.5 Middle
Finger Length

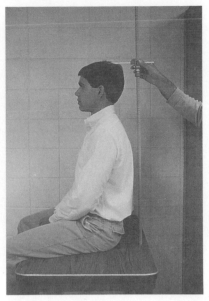

Figure 3.6 Sitting
Height

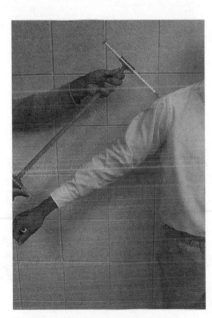

Figure 3.7 Arm Length

Figure 3.8 Head
Circumference

8. Arm Length: taken from the acromion process of the scapula to the styloid process of the ulna (each can be felt through the skin)(Figure 3.7).

D. The following are taken with a cloth tape.

9. Head Circumference: the maximum circumference of the head, not including the brow ridges (Figure 3.8).

37

Problems:

1. What are the differences between the sexes for the above measurements?

2. What are the differences between the left and right hand in each indivi-
    dual for Middle Finger Length? How does this correlate with handedness?

3. Compare standing height for each individual in the morning and again in
    late afternoon. How do the measurements compare?

4. Pick a measurement above, and everyone in the class measure the
    instructor. How did your measurement results vary? This is inter-obser-
    vor error.

5. Pick a measurement above, and measure one individual each day for two or
    three days or each week for two or three weeks. How did your measurement
    results vary? This is intra-observor error.

Chapter 4

Genetics

INTRODUCTION

Before we can really understand the mechanisms of evolution, we must understand how genetic information is passed from generation to generation.

Genetic information is carried within the nucleus of the cell. Chromosomes within the nucleus are made of coiled DNA (deoxyribonucleic acid) strands (see Figure 4.1).

Every human cell with a nucleus (except sperm and ova) contains 46 chromosomes, which carry all of the genetic information for the cell. These 46 chromosomes consist of 23 pairs, one pair is from the mother and one from the father. These are termed homologous chromosomes, which means that they each carry genetic information for the same trait at the same location. These homologous chromosomes, carry different alleles, however, and do not necessarily carry the same determinant for the trait. For instance, a particular location, or locus on each homologous chromosome codes for the condition of earlobe attachment, but one chromosome may carry the genetic code for attached earlobes, and the other chromosome may carry the code for free earlobes.

All cells in the body reproduce if they have a nucleus. Most of the cells in the body replicate throughout life by the process of mitosis, which results in two "daughter" cells, each carrying genetic information identical to the original cell. In this way, bones grow in a developing child, and skin heals itself after a cut.

41

Phenotype: Characteristic (or combination of characteristics) of an individual visually observed or discernable by other means (e.g. tallness in
garden peas, color blindness or blood type).   Individuals of the same
phenotype appear alike but may not have offspring of the same phenotype
(i.e., may have different genotypes).

Genotype: The genetic constitution (gene makeup), of an organism.

Gene: That section of DNA responsible for the ultimate synthesis of   a
specific polypeptide chain of amino acids; that portion of DNA with a
detectable function.

Allele: Alternative forms of a gene.   (Example: if the genotype of an individual is Aa for the trait of albinism, it contains two alleles determining this trait: A and a).

Homozygote: an organism whose chromosomes carry identical members of a given
pair of alleles.   The gametes are therefore all alike with respect to
this locus. (Example: AA or BB or aa).

Heterozygote: an organism with unlike members of any given pair or series of
at a particular locus.   Consequently this individual produces more than
one type of gamete (Example: Aa or Bb).

Dominant Allele: an allele which is expressed or measurable and which pre-
vents the expression of the recessive allele (i.e., masks recessive
alleles phenotypically).   A dominant allele is written in upper case
letters.

Recessive Allele: an allele which is not expressed or measurable when paired
with a dominant allele.   A recessive allele is written in lower case
letters.

Codominant Alleles: alleles which, when paired in an organism, are both
expressed.

Trait: one characteristic or aspect of a phenotype (example: hair color, ABO
blood type, eye color, etc.).

Certain cells participate in the reproduction of the individual by a process
of meiosis, which creates sex cells, or gametes (sperm or ova). Meiosis is
the method by which organisms transfer genetic information through generations, and is therefore important in our discussions of evolution.

We will not be concerned with describing in detail the different phases of
Mitosis (Prophase, Metaphase, Anaphase, Telophase) or Meiosis in this book, as
the individual phases are not as important in this level of discussion as to
know the outcome.   Those students who are interested in learning the specifics
of Mitosis or Meiosis should consult a genetics or biology textbook.

MITOSIS

Mitosis is a process of cell replication and division in which two daughter cells, each with a full complement of genetic information (46 chromosomes, or 23 pairs of chromosomes) is produced from a parent cell with 46 chromosomes.

Initially, before cell division occurs, an enzyme enters the DNA chains, and "unzips" the hydrogen bonds which hold the DNA bases together. A complete line of complementary bases to each side of the DNA chain is manufactured by the cell, so that after this process is finished, there exist two complete, identical lines of DNA. When seen in the "big" picture, each chromosome now has a copy, termed a chromatid). There are now 46 doubled chromosomes, or 92 chromatids.

As cell division proceeds, the chromatids line up along the "equator" of the nucleus, and the chromatids separate as cell division occurs. As the cell divides, the chromatids move away from each other, each to a different daughter cell. Each daughter cell now contains 46 chromosomes, still in 23 pairs. For a schematic diagram, see Figure 4.2.

MEIOSIS

The first cell division in meiosis also follows chromosomal duplication in the same manner as in mitosis. After duplication, each set of paired homologous chromosomes lines up along the equator of the nucleus, and as the cell undergoes the first division, each paired homologue separates, or segregates into its own daughter cell. After the first division, then, each daughter cell contains one of the homologous chromosomes, but each of these has two chromatids. Each of the daughter cells, in addition, contains only half of the genetic information which had been contained in the parent cell, hence this first division is also called reduction division. This first division is the important division in terms of evolution, as will be seen later.

The two daughter cells next undergo a second division in which the two chromatids of each of the 23 chromosomes separate into two more daughter cells. At the end of this division,

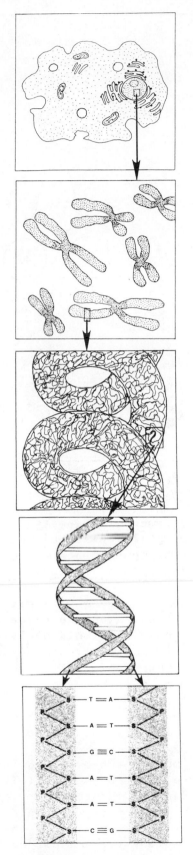

Figure 4.1 Magnification of Chromosome Strands

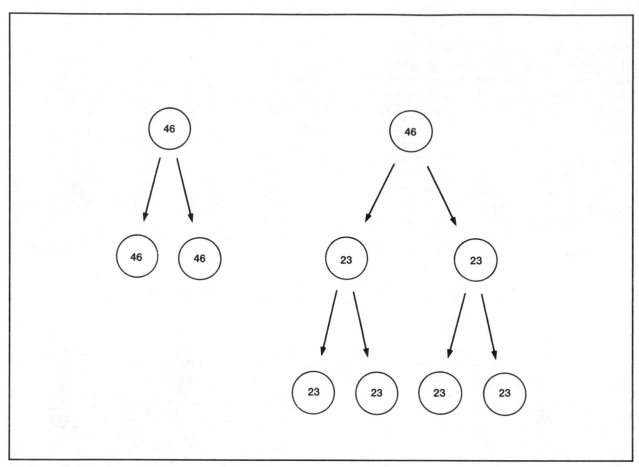

Figure 4.2 Schematic Drawings of Mitosis and Meiosis

then, each of 4 <u>gametes</u>, or sex cells, contains one copy of one chromosome of the original pair. In other words, each still contains half of the genetic information originally contained within the parent cell, and <u>contains only one copy of each of 23 chromosomes</u> (see Figure 4.2).

The above sequence in meiosis is typical of spermatogenesis, in that for each meiotic division, four sperm are formed. During the first division of oogenesis, however, only one viable, functional cell is produced, and that cell in turn produces only one viable, functional cell after the second division. The other nonviable cells are called <u>polar bodies</u>, and give up their cytoplasm (future nutrition for the fertilized zygote) to the one viable cell. The end result of oogenesis, then, is one gamete, the egg, which still has only half of the genetic information of the parent cell (as in spermatogenesis), but which is very much larger than a sperm cell.

Why must the gametes contain only half of the genetic information of an adult body cell? During fertilization of the egg by the sperm, the sperm injects its genetic information into the egg. Half of a zygote's genetic information (and therefore half of the child's genetic information) comes from the father, and half from the mother. Half of the genetic information which governs any trait (hair color, eye color, stature, I.Q., etc.) is contributed by the father, and half by the mother (except in sex-linked traits, to be explained later). Each half is in the form of one of the homologous chromosomes.

Before and during the first division of meiosis, several events can occur
which can alter the genetic configuration of the gametes, and therefore will
potentially alter the evolutionary outcome in a population. For instance, if a
mutation occurs during this time, (a point mutation, in which one base is
altered in a nucleotide, is the most common mutation) the genetic code in the
sperm or egg will be changed. Most mutations are deleterious or even lethal,
but are often neutral or seemingly neutral (that is, they will not alter the
selective advantages of the individual). Mutations which appear to be neutral
under one set of environmental circumstances however, may prove to be beneficial or maladaptive under others. Hence, if an environmental change occurs,
a neutral mutation is subjected to different selective pressures and may
consequently confer advantage or disadvantage to its carrier. Mutations are
also occasionally beneficial to the organism.

During the first division, paired homologous chromosomes may exchange genetic
material. This exchange, or crossing over, may alter the specific information
carried on a chromosome for a particular trait, and can greatly increase the
variation of information carried in the gametes.

Our further discussions in genetics will be concerned only with meiosis, and
variations in genotypes and phenotypes due to results of meiosis. Mitosis of
general body cells (bone, skin, etc.), though vital to life, is only indirec-
tly involved with evolution, as the results of mitotic divisions of these
cells are not passed from generation to generation.

Question: In what situation would a mutation in the mitotic division of a
body cell influence evolution? (Hint: it may be easier to answer this question
after the discussion on "Natural Selection").

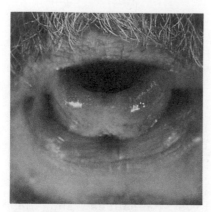

Figure 4.3 Tongue
Rolling

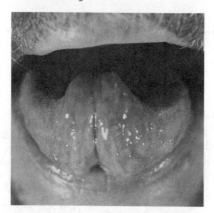

Figure 4.4 Tongue
Folding

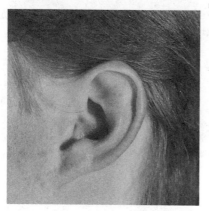

Figure 4.5 Attached
Earlobe

Most phenotypic traits are the results of a combination of effects of heredity and the environment. Skin color in an individual is determined to a large extent by genetic and racial background, but is also affected by the sun and even by diet. However, there are a small number of well-known traits which seem to be unaffected by the environment, and are useful in the study of genetic principles. Several of these are listed below:

1. The ability to taste PTC (Phenyl-thio-carbamide or Phenyl-thio-urea). This chemical is a man-made approximation of a naturally-occurring chemical which is known to suppress activity of the thyroid gland. PTC is found in turnips, kale, brussels sprouts, and has a bitter taste. Those individuals who can taste the chemical are therefore more likely to reject large amounts of those foods and to be less subject to goiter (Kitchin et al. 1959). The ability to taste PTC is inherited as a dominant.

2. The ability to roll the edges of one's tongue upward. This ability is inherited as a dominant.

3. Tongue folding: the ability to turn the tip of the tongue back upon the main body of the tongue without using the teeth. This trait is inherited as a recessive.

4. Earlobes: attached earlobes are characterized by the attachment of the lower part of the lobe to the skin of the head, while free-hanging lobes are not attached. The attached earlobe is inherited as a recessive.

5. Darwin's Tubercle: this is a projection on the helix of the ear, or a pointed thickening of the cartilage of the ear. The size of the projection varies, and it may be seen only on one of the ears. This trait is inherited as a dominant.

6. Hitchhiker's thumb: if, in the hitch-hiker's position one can bend the thumb back at an angle of 50 degrees or greater, he has inherited the trait as a recessive.

7. The ability to smell hydrocyanic acid (or potassium cyanide in solution). For obvious reasons (this material is extremely toxic), this will not be tested. This is inherited as a recessive (Montagu, 1960).

8. Interlocking fingers and thumbs: placing the left thumb over the right is inherited as a dominant characteristic. Forcing the condition opposite for that which you are genetically determined is uncomfortable.

Exercise:

Survey a sample of about 100 individuals for one or more of the traits listed. Fill in the following chart: the information will be used in exercises later.

Summary of Genetic Data for Sample

Trait	N	Number Dominant	Number Recessive	% Dom	% Rec
PTC Tasting	___	___	___	___	___
Tongue Rolling	___	212	___	___	___
Tongue Folding	___	___	145	___	___
Earlobes	___	___	56	___	___
Darwin's Tubercle	___	63	___	___	___
Hitchhiker Thumb	___	___	___	___	___
Hand Clasping	___	___	___	___	___

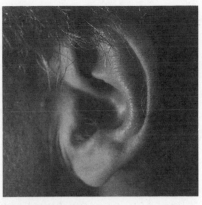

Figure 4.6 Free Earlobe

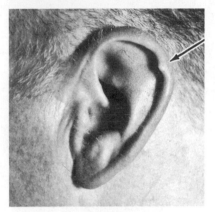

Figure 4.7 Darwin's Tubercle

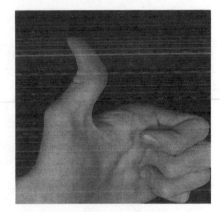

Figure 4.8 Hitchhiker's Thumb

Class total N = 270

tongue rolling : 212

tongue folding : 145

earlobes attached : 56

Darwins tubercles : 63

Right thumb on : 153
   top

GENETICS PROBLEMS

The key to solving genetics problems lies in remembering Gregor Mendel's <u>Principle of Segregation</u> and the <u>Principle of Independent Assortment</u>. Remember that during meiosis, or the formation of gametes (sex cells), the number of chromosomes in a cell is reduced from 46 to 23. Each pair of chromosomes thus separates and one chromosome goes to one gamete while the other goes to the other gamete. With the separation of chromosomes, the alleles for a two-allele trait (as we've been studying) also separate (as they reside on the chromosome). This is essentially Mendel's Principle of Segregation, that during meiosis the alleles separate. The Principle of Independent Assortment states that the members of different pairs of alleles assort independently into gametes. Obviously, the above principles are true only if the alleles in question are on separate chromosomes, however, so we will assume this fact in all of the following examples and exercises.

Suppose an individual possessed the two alleles Rr for the trait tongue-rolling. In the production of sex cells, these two alleles separate and go into two different gametes:

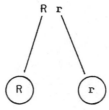

these are the gametes, or sex cells.

If you wanted to determine the genetics of an individual for two different traits, tongue rolling and tongue folding, for example, we could say that his genotype is: RrFf (write the alleles for each trait together; the dominant allele is written first). The alleles would separate into gametes as follows:

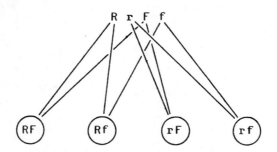

these are the gametes.

This second example uses the Principle of Independent Assortment, that is, regardless of how the alleles for tongue rolling segregate, the alleles for tongue folding will segregate independently, so that every combination possible will occur in different gametes.

48

1. An individual with a genotype Aa would create what gametes?

2. An individual with genotype AaBb would create what gametes?

3. An individual with a genotype AaBbCc would create what gametes?

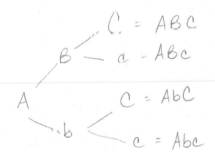

$$
A
\begin{cases}
B
\begin{cases}
C = ABC \\
c = ABc
\end{cases} \\
b
\begin{cases}
C = AbC \\
c = Abc
\end{cases}
\end{cases}
$$

$$
a
\begin{cases}
B
\begin{cases}
C = aBC \\
c = abc
\end{cases} \\
b
\begin{cases}
C = abC \\
c = abC
\end{cases}
\end{cases}
$$

<u>Answers:</u>

1.   The gametes would be:

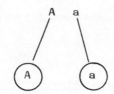

2.   The gametes would be:

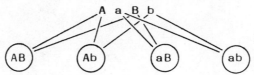

3.   The gametes would be:

(ABC) (ABc) (AbC) (Abc) (aBC) (aBc) (abC) (abc)

Hint: Another method sometimes used to predict the gamete combinations:

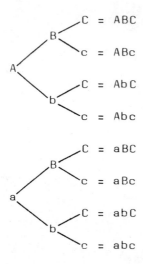

```
              C = ABC
          B
              c = ABc
      A
              C = AbC
          b
              c = Abc


              C = aBC
          B
              c = aBc
      a
              C = abC
          b
              c = abc
```

Once you have determined the gametes possible for each individual in your
mating pair, it's easy to figure out the results of matings between individuals, as all you do is put the different gametes into all of the possible
combinations.   One of the easiest ways to do this is by using the Punnett
Square.

<u>Example</u>   ⋅

What are the possible outcomes of a mating between individuals AaBb and AaBb?

Put the gametes along the top and side of the square and then cross-multiply.

	AB	Ab	aB	ab
AB	AABB	AABb	AaBB	AaBb
Ab	AABb	AAbb	AaBb 2	Aabb
aB	AaBB	AaBb 3	aaBB	aaBb
ab	AaBb 4	Aabb	aaBb	aabb

The results in this case are:

AABB(1) There were sixteen
AABb(2) individuals, and nine
AaBb(4) different genotypes. More
AAbb(1) interestingly, however, how
Aabb(2) many (and what kinds)
aaBB(1) phenotypes are there?
aaBb(2)
aabb(1)
AaBB(2)

Phenotypes:

AB (both traits dominant) = 9
Ab   = 3
aB   = 3
ab (both traits recessive = 1

Anytime you cross two individuals who are heterozygous for two traits, you will come up with a phenotype ratio of 9:3:3:1. Anytime you cross two individuals who are heterozygous for three traits, you will come up with a phenotype ratio of 27:9:9:9:3:3:3:1. (Try it!)

Problems: Gamete Formation
Show your work

1. What are the gametes for individual AABB?

 × 4

2. What are the gametes for individual AaBB?

3. What are the gametes for individual aabb?

4. What are the gametes for individual aabbcc?

5. What are the gametes for individual AaBbCc?

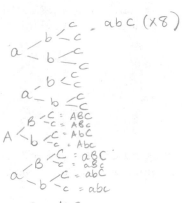

6. What are the gametes for individual AAbbCc?

A < b < C = AbC
        c = Abc
    b < C = AbC
        c = Abc

A < b < c = Abc
    b < C = Abc
        c = Abc

3 AbC
5 Abc

Genotype Formations — NEED DATA FROM CLASS

1. What are the possible genotypes for each of the phenotypes tested in the
    survey on page 47?

2. What are the genotypes of the offspring possible from a mating of Rr X Rr?

53

3. What are the genotypes of the offspring possible for a mating of RR X rr?

$$
\begin{array}{c|cc}
 & R & R \\
\hline
r & Rr & Rr \\
r & Rr & Rr \\
\end{array}
$$

4. What percentage of the offspring from a mating of two individuals each heterozygous for Tongue Rolling and PTC tasting will be able both to roll the tongue and taste PTC?

TtPp × TtPp

9:3:3:1   9/16 ≈ 56%

4.b. What percentage of the offspring from the above mating will be able neither to roll the tongue nor taste PTC?

1/16 = 6.2%

4.c. What percentage of the offspring from the above mating will be hetero-zygous for both traits?

4/16 = 25%

5. What percentage of the offspring from a mating of two individuals each heterozygous for Tongue Rolling, PTC tasting and Tongue Folding will have none of the three traits?

- homozygous recessive for all traits

1/64 = 1.6%

PEDIGREE ANALYSIS

When a researcher comes across a subject who phenotypically shows a trait that the researcher knows to be dominant, as we've seen, the subject can genetically be either homozygous dominant or heterozygous for that trait. The specific genotype cannot be determined without looking into the individual's family to determine the genetic consistution of the ancestors (or, less practically, by letting the subject mate and recording future distribution of the traits). Likewise, if, for instance, a physician is concerned that a patient is a carrier of a recessive trait (but the trait is not phenotypically visible), the only way to determine the presence of the recessive allele is by pedigree analysis, or by reconstructing the "family tree" to show the distribution of that particular trait within the family group. To a certain extent the geneticist can predict the possible outcomes of future matings with the help of these analyses.

In pedigree analysis, males are indicated by squares, females by circles, and those persons of unknown sex by diamonds. Matings are represented by horizontal lines to the middle of the circle or square, whereas vertical lines indicate descent. Children are listed from eldest to youngest, from left to right. Twins are represented by lines from a common point, while deceased individuals are often shown with a diagonal line through a symbol.

Individuals phenotypically showing the trait in question are indicated by blackened symbols. In the case of dominant inheritance, the individual who exhibits a trait must have at least one parent who also shows it. If only one parent shows the trait, the individual in question must be heterozygous for it. Because of the rule of dominant inheritance, an individual who exhibits the dominant trait will have at least one parent who also shows it.

If an individual showing a recessive trait has two parents neither of whom shows the trait, both parents must be carriers of one recessive and one dominant allele (i.e. heterozygous). The recessive traits are, therefore, not found in every generation.

Warning: a recessive condition with a substantial gene frequency will sometimes mimic a dominant trait in a pedigree chart. In the following exercises, however, assume the typical situation described above.

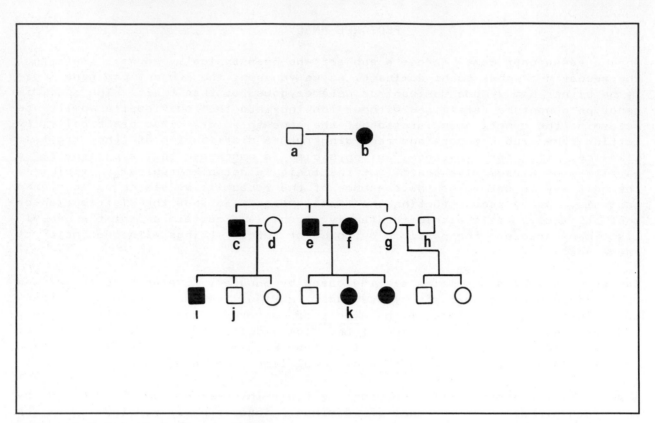

Figure 4.9 Case A Pedigree Chart

Sample Problem

1. Is this trait inherited as a dominant or a recessive?

2. What are the probable genotypes of individuals a and b?

3. If individual a had married an individual of the same genotype as himself, how many of the children from this mating would show the trait (what percentage)?

Answers:

1. In the case of dominant inheritance, any individual who shows the trait must have at least one parent who shows the trait. Notice that this is true in this problem, therefore the trait is inherited as a dominant.
2. a. aa
    b. Aa
3. None of the children would show the trait.

1. In Case A, what are the genotypes of individuals c through k?

        c.   g.   k.
        d.   h.
        e.   i.
        f.   j.

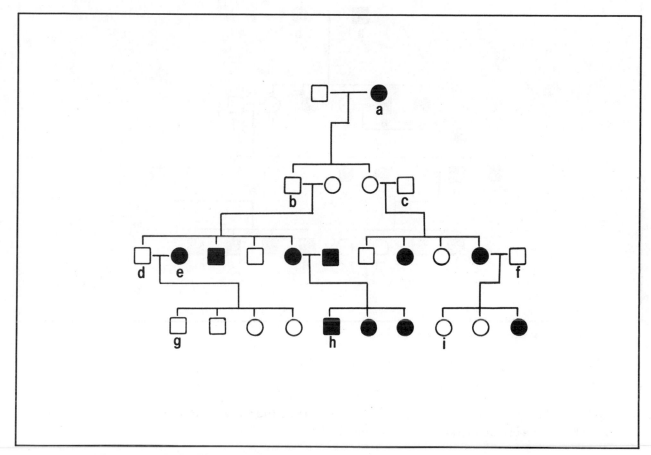

Figure 4.10 Case B Pedigree Chart

1. Is this trait dominant or recessive?

2. What are the possible genotypes of individuals a through i?

        a.   f.
        b.   g.
        c.   h.
        d.   i.
        e.

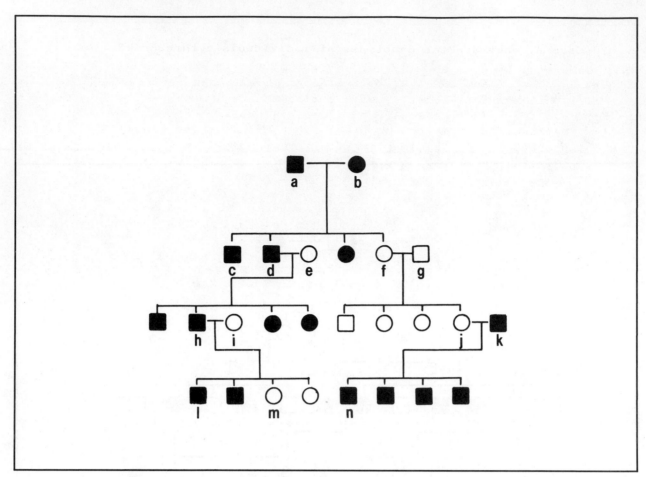

Figure 4.11 Case C Pedigree Chart

Problems

1. Is this trait dominant or recessive?

2. What are the possible genotypes of individuals a through n?

a.	f.	k.
b.	g.	l.
c.	h.	m.
d.	i.	n.
e.	j.	

Several genes are said to be <u>sex-linked</u> when they occur on those chromosomes which determine the sex of an individual, the X or Y chromosomes (the 23rd of the 23 pairs of chromosomes). A female receives two X chromosomes from her parents, while a male receives an X chromosome from his mother and a Y from his father. Most of the sex-linked genes are carried on the X chromosome, as the Y chromosome carries few of the loci of the X chromosome. For several traits, therefore, a female with two X chromosomes will carry a pair of alleles for a trait while a male, who has an XY configuration will carry only one allele of a trait. Hence the male has a greater chance of phenotypically showing a sex-linked trait.

Notice in the following pedigree chart that no women in the family group expressed the trait shown.

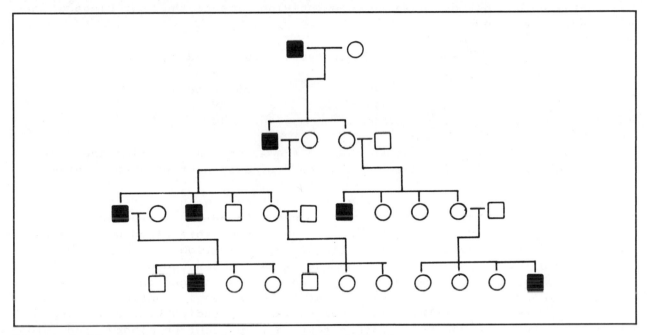

Figure 4.12   Pedigree Chart for Sex-Linked Trait

Defective color vision, or color blindness, is a sex-linked trait, as is hemophilia, or bleeder's disease. One type of night blindness, a form of nystagmus (an involuntary oscillation of the eyeball), and several other (around 120) conditions and diseases are now known to be sex-linked. (Gardner, 1975).

A red-green color blind man has a single recessive allele in his X chromosome. The Y chromosome carries no locus for this trait, so whatever allele form is carried by the X chromosome will determine the man's phenotype. If this man marries a woman who is homozygous dominant (i.e. normal), all of the daughters will be carriers of the trait, but will be phenotypically normal. The sons will all be normal, and will not carry the trait.

<u>Sample Problem</u>:

Why will all of the sons of a marriage between a red-green color blind man and a woman who is homozygous dominant for the trait (i.e. normal) be normal?

The homozygous normal woman can only give a normal allele to any off-spring, sons or daughters. The Y chromosome passed by the father to the sons carries NO allele for the trait, so the mother's normal allele passed to the son will be expressed. The color-blind man will, however, pass a recessive allele on the X chromosome inherited by his daughters, making them carriers.

BLOOD TYPING

The ABO blood group system is one of the best understood multiple allele systems. All of the ABO blood types are determined by two genetically determined proteins called **antigens**; the A antigen and the B antigen. These proteins occur on the surface of the red blood cells. An individual's blood may contain one, both, or neither of these antigens, giving rise to the four blood groups: A, B, AB, O, as shown:

Blood Group (phenotype)	Genotype
A	AA or AO
B	BB or BO
AB	AB
O	OO

As one can surmise from the above chart, the A and the B alleles are dominant to the O allele, while the A and B alleles are codominant with one another.

Individuals with blood group A have the A antigen on the red blood cells, those with group B have the B antigen, those with AB blood type have both the A and B antigens, and those with genotype OO have neither blood group antigen. Antibodies destroy antigens, resulting in agglutination, or clumping of the red blood cells, so in this case, the anti-A antibodies cause agglutination of the A and the AB blood types, as both have the A antigen on the red blood cells. Likewise, the anti-B antibodies will cause agglutination of the B and the AB blood types. Neither anti-A nor anti-B antibodies will cause agglutination of type O blood, as neither antigen is present on those red blood cells.

Following is a chart which should make these combinations easier to understand.

Antigen-Antibody Combinations

Blood Group	Contains Antigens: A	B	Will react against: Antibodies Anti-A	Anti-B	Will Create: Antibodies Against: A	B
A	X		X			X
B		X		X	X	
AB	X	X	X	X		
O					X	X

Blood group O, as can be seen from this chart, contains neither antigen, so is commonly referred to as the "universal donor," as the host antibodies can find nothing against which to react. Conversely, individuals with blood group AB will create antibodies against neither antigen (because it contains both antigens on its blood cells and would not make antibodies against its own blood). Because of this, type AB is commonly referred to as the "universal recipient."

The distribution of blood groups varies in different areas of the world, and among different racial groups. Europeans most commonly have either blood group A or O (about 40% each), about 15% have type B blood, and around 5% show type AB blood. The highest frequency of type A blood occurs in the Blackfoot Indians of North America and the Lapps in northern Scandinavia. The lowest frequency of type A blood occurs in the Central and South American Indians. In most of the world the frequency of type A blood is about 10% to 35%. The highest frequency of type B blood occurs in central Asia, and it is virtually absent among American Indians and Australian Aborigines. In most of the world the frequency of type B blood is about 5% to 25% (Mourant 1954, Mourant et al. 1958).

You will be typing your blood in this lab. This is a fairly simple procedure (as are the genetics to explain it), but the rules for typing the blood must be strictly followed so as to avoid contamination (either of you or your blood sample). If, at anytime, you feel faint or ill during this exercise, lie down until the feeling passes.

IF YOU HAVE A DISEASE WHICH COULD BE SPREAD THROUGH CONTACT WITH YOUR BLOOD, DO NOT PARTICIPATE IN THIS EXERCISE!

1. The following materials will be provided: alcohol, cotton balls, sterile gauze, sterile blood lancets, a clean microscope slide, toothpick, and the bottles of antiserum.

2. Wash your hands and swab alcohol over the finger from which you will draw your blood sample. Be sure the alcohol is dry on your finger before you prick it, as if alcohol contaminates your blood sample, the results of the test may be altered.

3. Prick your finger (or have the lab instructor do it for you). Throw the lancet away. NEVER USE A LANCET TWICE, NEVER USE A LANCET PREVIOUSLY USED BY SOMEONE ELSE, AND NEVER JUST LEAVE IT ON THE TABLE!

4. Wipe your finger with the sterile gauze after the first small drop of blood. This first drop may contain only a few red blood cells. Place a drop of blood at each end of the microscope slide.

5. Place a drop of anti-A on one drop of blood, and a drop of anti-B on the other drop of blood. Never touch the tip of the eye dropper to the blood. Take a clean toothpick and mix the antiserum with the blood sample, taking care to use a clean toothpick for each drop of blood.

6. Note the agglutination of each sample in the first three minutes of the test (otherwise coagulation may take place and confuse the observation of agglutination).

Fill in the following chart: Mark agglutination with +

Anti-A   Anti-B

Compare   this chart with the "Antigen-Antibody Combinations" chart to find
your blood type.

Sample Problem

A man has been taken to trial in a paternity suit by a woman who claims
that he is the father of her son. The man claims innocence. At the trial
the expert witness disclosed the blood types of all three, as follows:

> The woman: Type A
> The man: Type B
> The child: Type O

Could the man be the father of the child?

Answer:

First list the possible genotypes of each of the above blood types, as
follows:

> The woman: Genotypes AA or AO
> The man: Genotypes B or BO
> The child: Genotype OO

If the woman possessed genotype AO and if the man had BO, then the cross could
look like this:

	B	O
A	AB	AO
O	BO	OO

As 1/4 of the offspring are likely to be genotype OO, or blood type O, then
the man <u>could</u> be the father. However, any other man with blood types B, A, or
O (though not AB: why?) could be the father, so this man cannot be indicted on
this evidence alone.

Problems

1.   Mr. and Mrs. Jones have just come home from the hospital with their first
     child, but they are very disturbed because their friends say the baby
     looks like neither of them. Have they come home with the wrong baby?
     Blood samples are taken, and they are:

          Mrs. Jones: A
          Mr. Jones: O
          Baby: AB

     Could they be the baby's natural parents?

2.   John and Barry are out hiking, when Barry falls down a cliff and severs a
     major artery. At the hospital, John offers to donate his blood for a
     direct transfusion for Barry. John has type O blood, and Barry has type
     A. Strictly on the basis of blood type, should the hospital accept or
     refuse John's offer? Why?

3.   John and Barry are out hiking again, and this time John falls and is
     hurt. Barry offers to return the favor of a blood transfusion at the
     hospital. Should the hospital accept or reject Barry's offer? Why?

EVOLUTION AND THE HARDY-WEINBERG FORMULA

Evolution is said to be occurring when an allele frequency changes from one generation to the next in a population. Factors which produce and redistribute variation in a population include:

a. <u>Mutation</u>: an actual alteration in genetic material. This is the basic creative force in evolution and is the only way to produce new variation in a population.

b. <u>Migration</u>: a movement of genes from one population to another, also termed <u>gene flow</u>.

c. <u>Genetic Drift</u>: an effect of sampling error, that is, to reduced chances in a very small population of the next generation having the same proportion of alleles as occurred in the parent generation. For example, if 5 people in a population of 30 were unable to roll his or her tongue, what is the probability that in the next generation 5 people would again be unable to tongue-roll? The effects of random distribution of alleles for the next generation are not as noticeable in very large populations.

d. <u>Founder Effect</u>: a severe form of genetic drift. For example, if 10 of the people in our population of 30 sailed in a boat together and crashed on a deserted island, and if all of the five people who are unable to tongue-roll were on that boat, a new population would be started consisting of 50% tongue-rollers and 50% of those unable to roll the tongue. The future generation would be very unlike the original population.

The above forces act to produce variation in a population.

e. <u>Natural Selection</u>: a process which acts on this variation. If there is variation in a population, some of these variations may influence reproductive success (numbers of offspring successfully raised to have offspring of their own). Natural Selection may, then, be defined as differential net reproductive success. The unit of natural selection is the individual, the unit of evolution is the population. Those individuals best adapted to an environment will be the ones who survive to pass their genetic information to the next generation, while those who are not so adapted will be selected against, and will not pass their genes to the next generation. Therefore, adaptation is a shift in gene frequencies due to function.

All of the above factors in a particular environment describe situations in which gene frequencies change in a population from generation to generation, i.e. the population is evolving. If a population is not evolving, we can define that genetic equilibrium in terms of a mathematical model, the <u>Hardy-Weinberg</u> formula. The most simple form of this equation contains two allele frequencies, p and q, which describe the simple kind of trait discussed so far. These two alleles are the only determinants of the trait, so the frequencies are represented by: $p + q = 1$. The Hardy-Weinberg formula, or the description of the various combinations of these allele frequencies is shown by the following binomial ("two names") equation.

$$p^2 + 2pq + q^2 = 1.$$

This formula also equals 1 because these are the only combinations which can describe the way these two alleles combine, and therefore must equal unity, or one. P (or p) denotes the dominant allele, q denotes the recessive, and the frequencies are:

$$p^2, \quad pq, \quad \text{and} \quad q^2.$$

Remember during the following discussions that $p^2 = pp = p \times p$, and that
  p = the frequency of the dominant allele, while
  q = the frequency of the recessive allele.
In tongue-rolling,
  R denotes the dominant allele, while
  r denotes the recessive allele.

We are primarily interested in the Hardy-Weinberg formula, though, because it can be used to calculate the frequencies of the various alleles in a population, as long as we can assume genetic equilibrium. In our studies so far, we have used both the 2-allele traits, (or those traits determined by two alleles such as tongue rolling, tongue folding, PTC tasting, etc.) and the 3-allele traits, such as the ABO blood grouping system.

First, an example from the 2-allele system:

Suppose we have taken a survey from campus and have found that 75 out of 100 (or 75%) students are able to roll their tongues. By now we are able to determine that the possible genotypes are: **RR**, **Rr**, and **rr**. Since tongue rolling is a dominant trait, those able to roll their tongues have either genotype RR or Rr, while those not able to roll have genotype rr. Therefore, our genotypes are:

rr = 25% or .25
RR and Rr = 75% or .75

The first step in determining the frequencies of the genotypes (p^2, $2pq$, q^2) in a population is to figure out the allele frequencies (p,q). Do not forget this rule: Always (when working with a dominant-recessive situation) start with the homozygous recessive, in this case rr.

We want the allele frequency, q, and we know the r genotype frequency, q^2.

Because $q = \sqrt{q^2}$, in this case $q = \sqrt{.25}$ or .5. This, remember, describes the allele r in our formula, so we have determined one allele frequency.
Since p + q = 1, then 1 - .5 = p, so p = .5 as well.

We just plug these numbers into our formula:

$$p^2 + 2pq + q^2 = 1$$
$$\text{so } (.5)^2 + 2(.5)(.5) + (.5)^2 = 1$$
$$\text{and } (.25) + (.50) + (.25) = 1$$

corresponds to: RR Rr rr : our genotypes. We have just determined the genotype frequencies in our population in genetic equilibrium!

Note: the Hardy-Weinberg formula gives expected frequencies when the population is in genetic equilibrium. The real frequencies may vary.

In the 3-allele system, simply add another allele to your formula: so that $p + q + r = 1$, and now the Hardy-Weinberg formula reads:

$$p^2 + 2pq + q^2 + 2pr + 2qr + r^2 = 1.$$

As stated before, in the ABO blood system, A and B are dominant to O, but A and B are co-dominant. Hence, the phenotypes possible for the system are: A, B, AB, and O, but the genotypes possible are:

Phenotype	Genotypes
A	AA, AO
B	BB, BO
AB	AB
O	OO

In this example, p = the frequency of A, q = the frequency of B, and r = the frequency of O.

Remember the above rule to figure out the allele frequencies: Always start with the homozygous recessive, in this case OO. So, since we are looking for the frequency (r) of the O allele, then $r = \sqrt{rr}$.
Next, we need to find the frequencies (p, q) of the other alleles (A and B):

$$r = \sqrt{OO}$$

$$p = \sqrt{\text{Genotype freqs. } AA + AO + OO} - \text{Allele freq. O, or, stated another way:}$$

$$p = \sqrt{\text{Phenotype freqs. } A + O} - \text{Allele freq. O.}$$

then: $q = 1 - (p + r)$.

This formula is not as bad as it looks when you think about what you are trying to do. You need to determine the allele frequencies. Some individuals who are phenotypically A and B are heterozygotes, and therefore carry an unexpressed O allele. Therefore, in order to study only allele A or allele B, you need to eliminate the contribution of allele O from those phenotypes. That is the purpose of the formula: $p = \sqrt{\text{phenotypes } A + O} - \text{phenotype O.}$ *Allele frequency*

Example: You have taken a sample of 100 Europeans and found that the blood type frequencies are (remember, these are the phenotypes):

$$A = 40\% \text{ or } .40 \text{ (genotypes AA, AO)}$$
$$B = 15\% \text{ or } .15 \text{ (genotypes BB, BO)}$$
$$AB = 5\% \text{ or } .05 \text{ (genotype AB)}$$
$$O = 40\% \text{ or } .40 \text{ (genotype OO)}$$

$$r = \sqrt{OO} = \sqrt{.40} = .632$$

$$p = \sqrt{\text{phenotypes } A + O} - O$$
$$= \sqrt{.40 + .40} - .632$$
$$= \sqrt{.80} - .632$$
$$= .894 - .632$$
$$= .262$$

```
                         q = 1 - (p + r)
                           = 1 - (.262 + .632)
                           = 1 - .894
                           = .106
```

So the allele frequencies are:

```
                         r = .632
                         p = .262
                         q = .106
```

When plugged into the Hardy-Weinberg formula to find the genotype frequencies:

$$p^2 + 2pq + q^2 + 2pr + 2qr + r^2 = 1$$

$$(.26)^2 + 2(.26)(.11) + (.11)^2 + 2(.26)(.63) + 2(.11)(.63) + (.63)^2 = 1$$

```
   = .07    .06    .01    .33    .14    .40      are the genotypes and
      AA     AB     BB     AO     BO     OO      genotype frequencies.
```

Problems:

1. Iodine is physiologically important because it is necessary for the pro-
    duction of the thyroid hormone (thyroxin) which plays a major role in
    regulating metabolic activity. The World Health Organization is inter-
    ested in this fact because they have found that a mutation has occurred
    on the imaginary island of Pika Pika in the South Pacific which enables
    the islanders to withstand very low levels of iodine in the diet
    while maintaining adequate levels of thyroxin for metabolism. You, as
    a qualified anthropologist, are asked to find the frequency of
    individuals on the island with this mutation. Assuming that this trait
    is controlled by a single gene (two alleles), you find that 36 out
    of 100 individuals on this island have this mutation. Assume also
    that this trait shows up as a recessive.

    a. Find the frequencies (p and q) of alleles R and r.

    b. Find the genotype frequencies (p^2, $2pq$ and q^2).

2. After finding the above frequencies, it was found that 64 percent of the
    individuals on this island are unable to eat conch chowder because of a
    mutation prohibiting them from digesting enzymes present in the conch
    flesh. This is very distressing to the Pika Pika government, as they
    plan to raise conch commercially as a food crop. The gene frequencies
    and genotype frequencies will tell them if it is feasible to go ahead
    with their plans to market conch. Assume that the 64% show homozygous
    recessive condition.

    a. Find the frequencies (p and q) of alleles T and t.

    b. Find the genotype frequencies (p^2, $2pq$ and q^2).

69

3. You have gone to Africa and have found that the blood group frequencies
    are: (these are phenotypes)

    A: 36%
    B: 16%
    AB: 4%
    O: 44%

    a. Find the allele frequencies.

    b. Find the genotype frequencies.

4. In a given population the frequency of allele A is 0.2 and of allele B is
    0.3. What are the frequencies of the blood types A, B, AB and O?

5. Using the numbers obtained in your survey of 100 individuals for the
    sample Mendelian traits (page 47), what are the probable genotype
    frequencies of your sample for these traits?

PROBABILITY

We have stated that the Hardy-Weinberg formula is simply a binomial equation. We can also use the binomial equation to answer the question:

> If a couple has two children, what is the probability that both of them will be boys (or, out of 2 tosses of a coin, what is the probability that both outcomes will be heads?)

We can use the bionomial equation because the children will be either boys or girls (remember, "binomial = two names," and the results are mutually exclusive).

For this question, we start by multiplying (p+q) by itself two times for the two combinations of possible outcomes:

$$(p+q)^2 = p^2 + 2pq + q^2 = 1$$

(again, it must equal unity, as these are all of the outcomes possible in our sample).

If we let p = boys and q = girls, and if we let the superscript equal the resultant number of either boys or girls, we have the probabilities:

$$1/4 = p^2 = 2 \text{ boys}$$

$$2/4 = pq = 1 \text{ boy, } 1 \text{ girl}$$

$$1/4 = q^2 = 2 \text{ girls.}$$

Therefore there is a 25% probability that out of two children, both will be boys.

As an aid to figuring the coefficient of each term (e.g. in the figure 2pq, "2" is the coefficient in front of "pq," the term), we may use Pascal's triangle.

Number of trials

```
                              1

1.                    1             1

2.                 1       2       1

3.              1      3      3       1

4.           1     4      6      4      1

5.        1     5    10      10     5      1

6.     1     6    15     20     15     6     1
```

For each layer, add the two adjacent numbers above the number you need.

Example: Out of 5 children, (5 trials), the binomial equation would look like this:

$$p^5 + 5p^4q + 10p^3q^2 + 10p^2q^3 + 5pq^4 + q^5$$

(To determine superscripts, always, from right to left, add one each time to q and substract one for p).

Sample Problem:

What is the probability that out of 5 children, 4 would be boys?

Answer:

We look for the term with 4 boys and 1 girl, or $5p^4q$. The coefficient is 5; the total number of possibilities is 32 (add the coefficients: 1+5+10+10+5+1= 32), so the probability of 4 boys and 1 girl = 5/32, or 15%.

It should seem obvious that even though the probability of the above occurrence is 15%, those results are not guaranteed. Likewise, in a series of coin tosses, one would expect that 1/2 of the results would be heads, and 1/2 would be tails. In a very large number of tosses, (n = 100,000) those results would be very likely, but the likelihood of heads equaling exactly 50% decreases as the sample size decreases. Try a series of 10 tosses each. How many times were the results exactly 50% heads? These differences from the expected are the result of **sampling error**.

Sampling error also provides the basis for relatively drastic changes in the genetic frequencies within and between populations. Assortative mating, migration or gene flow, and genetic drift and its severe form, founder effect are all examples of sampling error on the level of the population, in which the genotypes of the sample are accidentally or purposely different from the frequencies of the parent population.

ASSORTATIVE MATING

Example: Suppose that out of 100 individuals, 36 could not roll his or her tongue, and that those individuals were considered to be inferior by those who could roll the tongue. Therefore, the individuals who were genotype rr would marry each other, and those who were RR or Rr would likewise marry each other. How would the genotype and allele frequencies change in the following generation in this population?

Answer: In the original population, 36% of the individuals were genotype rr, so the frequency for $r = \sqrt{.36} = .6$, Therefore, R = 1-.6 = .4 The genotype frequencies for the original population would be:

$$RR + 2Rr + rr = 1$$

$$(.4)^2 + 2(.4)(.6) + (.6)^2 = 1$$

$$.16 \qquad .48 \qquad .36 = 1$$

The number of individuals for each genotype is:

$$RR = .16 \ (100) = 16 = 16\%$$
$$Rr = .48 \ (100) = 48 = 48\%$$
$$rr = .36 \ (100) = 36 = 36\% \ (rr \ already \ discovered)$$

Daughter (F1) Generations:

Tongue-Rollers Group	¶	Non-Rollers Group
	¶	
	¶	
RR + 2Rr + rr	¶	RR + 2Rr + rr
	¶	
	¶	
	¶	
R = .16 + 1/2(.48) = .40	¶	R = 00 + 1/2(00) = 0
r = .00 + 1/2(.48) = .24	¶	r = .36 + 1/2(00) = .36

Cultural boundary

When the values for the r allele within the entire population (the sum of the two groups), r=.36 + .24 = .60.

As can be seen, the genotype frequencies change within each breeding segment of the population, but allele frequencies in the entire population do not change. The dominant genotypes become more frequent in one population, while the recessive genotypes become more frequent in the other breeding population. the heterozygous condition becomes less and less frequent.

MIGRATION OR GENE FLOW

Example: Suppose 10 individuals (5 men and 5 women) who were all homozygous dominant for tongue rolling migrated into a population of 100 individuals in which 36 individuals could not roll the tongue. How would the gene frequencies of the next generation from random matings of the new population be different from the original population?

Answer: In the original population, 36% of the individuals were genotype rr, so the frequency for r = $\sqrt{.36}$ = .6, therefore the frequency of p = 1 - .6 = .4.

The genotype frequencies for the original population would be:

RR	+	2Rr	+	rr	= 1
$(.4)^2$	+	$2(.4)(.6)$	+	$(.6)^2$	= 1
.16		.48		.36	= 1

The number of individuals for each genotype is:

$$RR = .16 \ (100) = 16 = 16\%$$
$$Rr = .48 \ (100) = 48 = 48\%$$
$$rr = .36 \ (100) = 36 = 36\% \ (rr \ already \ discovered)$$

73

If the individuals who migrated into the population are all genotype RR (discovered from their past records), then the numbers for the new population are:

$$RR = 16 + 10 = 26/110 = 24\%$$
$$Rr = 48 = 0 = 48/110 = 44\%$$
$$rr = 36 = 0 = 36/110 = 33\%$$

New allele frequencies are:

$$r = \sqrt{.33} = .57$$
$$R = 1 - .57 = .43$$

GENETIC DRIFT AND FOUNDER EFFECT

Since Founder Effect is essentially a drastic form of Genetic Drift, we shall show an example of the former. Both, again, are examples of sampling error.

Example:

Out of 100 individuals in our population, 36 cannot roll the tongue. Ten of the individuals in this population decided to go on an ocean cruise together, and they were stranded on a deserted island for 20 years. It just happens that 7 of these stranded individuals are not tongue-rollers, a genotype frequency which is vastly different from the original population.

But, what about the original population after the next generation? How have the genotype and allele frequencies changed?

$$\text{Population number:} \quad 100 - 10 = 90$$

$$rr = 36 - 7 = 29/90 = 32\%$$
$$RR \ \& \ Rr = 61/90 = 68\%$$

$$r = \sqrt{.32} = .57$$
$$R = 1 - .57 = .43$$

$$RR + 2Rr + rr = 1$$

$$(.43)^2 + 2(.43)(.57) + (.57)^2 = 1$$

$$.18 \qquad .49 \qquad .32$$

Obviously, the smaller the population, the more drastic the effect after the loss of a number of individuals.

Problems:

1. What is the probability that out of 3 children, 2 will be boys?

2. What is the probability that out of 5 coin tosses, 2 will be heads?

3. Suppose that out of a population of 100 individuals, 25 could not taste PTC and that the individuals in that population who could taste this chemical decided only to marry other individuals who could taste PTC. How would the genotype and allele frequencies change in the second generation?

    This is an example of what evolutionary force?

4. The example on pages 63 and 64 shows a fairly drastic change in allele and genotype frequencies, but suppose another group of 10 individuals entered the population after the next generation, all homozygous dominant for the trait of tongue rolling. What are the genotype frequencies and allele frequencies for the new population?

5. Suppose that a small island population of 100 individuals is visited by 25 sailors who decide to stay and raise families. Suppose also that 36% of the original population are unable to roll their tongues, and that none of the sailors are able to roll their tongues. What will be the genotype and allele frequencies of the next generation?

    This is an example of what kind of evolutionary force?

6. Suppose that 35% of a population of 100 individuals has hitchhiker's thumb, which is inherited as a recessive. Suppose also, that 10 individuals, 5 of whom have the hitchhiker's thumb decide to go deep sea fishing and are stranded on a deserted island for at least a generation, and that all stranded individuals mate. What are the genotype and allele frequencies of both new populations in the next generation?

    This is an example of what kind of evolutionary force?

THE PARADIGM DEBATE IN EVOLUTIONARY THEORY

The theories of evolutionary change presented so far have had their beginnings in ideas popularized by Charles Darwin in the middle of the 19th century, and have been termed the "Gradualism Paradigm." Gradualism was incorporated into a modern synthesis of natural selection and genetics in the 1930s and 40s, the result of which was population genetics. Briefly, this paradigm suggests that mutations are the ultimate source of new variation in populations, and that favorable mutations are gradually spread throughout the species by gene flow. In this way a species is always gradually evolving, that is, gene frequencies are continuously changing in populations and within the species as a whole.

In the 1970s two paleontologists, S.J. Gould and Niles Eldredge, introduced a new paradigm: Punctuated Equilibrium (Eldredge and Gould 1972, Gould and Eldredge 1977), in which they claimed that data from the fossil record does not fit into the gradualism paradigm. They stated that many, if not most, fossil records indicate that the morphology of a species often is in stasis, and does not change for long periods of time (sometimes for millions of years), to be "punctuated" suddenly by the appearance of a new species. The change to a new species (speciation) occurs quite rapidly, perhaps in only a few thousand years (quite rapid in the geological time scale). Gould and Eldredge further suggest that speciation might occur in a small peripheral population that is genetically separated from the parent population. After speciation the new species may or may not replace the parent species. The fact that speciation occurs in very small populations in a small part of the geographical range of the species, according to the theory, accounts for the relative paucity of fossils that show a transition from one species to another. As we shall see, there are some possible transitional fossils in the hominid record, but they are rare relative to the number of speciation events that have occurred. Since only a very small percentage of all organisms are ever fossilized, it is even more unlikely that transitional organisms in the small populations where speciation events occur will be fossilized.

Below is a brief list of the essential features of each paradigm:

Gradualism	Punctuated Equilibrium
1. Species change as a whole	1. Speciation in small, peripheral groups on edges of their econiches
2. Changes are continuous and occur in small steps	2. Species experience long periods of stasis
3. Change is directional; moves toward better adaptation	3. Speciation is random change, not necessarily better; not markedly harmful
4. Speciation rate may vary, but occurs after sufficient small changes	4. Speciation occurs rather quickly in geologic time
5. Imperfect fossil record omits most intermediate steps	5. Imperfect fossil record usually doesn't record swift changes in small populations

77

Recently a group of evolutionary biologists met in Germany and debated the above paradigms. They concluded that "...there is no question that both stasis with punctuation and gradual continuous morphological evolution occur; the debate concerns the relative frequency of extremes of these modes..." (Maderson et al. 1982: 286). It would appear that elements of both paradigms will be a part of the theory of evolution.

We will return to this debate when we examine the fossil record for later stages of human evolution.

Chapter 5

Biological Classification

INTRODUCTION

Classification systems are developed because they improve communication.

Biological classification is based on the system established by the Swedish Naturalist Carolus Linnaeus (Karl von Linne, 1707-1778). Linnaeus used the Latin language in his biological classification system, and assigned each organism a Latin binomial ("two names"): a genus and species. Our biological name, for example is <u>Homo sapiens</u> (Latin for "wise man"). The first letter of the genus (pl. genera) is always capitalized, the species always begins with a lowercase letter, and the entire name is italicized or underlined in print. When referring to an organism, the genus and species names must be used, though the genus may be abbreviated by using only the first letter (capitalized) when there is no danger of confusion (e.g., <u>H. sapiens</u>).

Linnaeus established a formal hierarcy for establishing taxa ([sing. taxon], a general term for any Linnaean category) above the level of species. While Linnaeus himself devised this hierarcy more than a century before the theory of evolution was proposed by Darwin and Wallace, most biological taxonomists today classify organisms according to their evolutionary relationships (phylogeny). While our genus today contains only one species, the genus for chimpanzees contains two closely related species, <u>Pan troglodytes</u> (common chimpanzee) and <u>Pan paniscus</u> (bonobo chimpanzee). Genera themselves are grouped into related families, families into related superfamilies, superfamilies into related orders, orders into related classes, and so on.

79

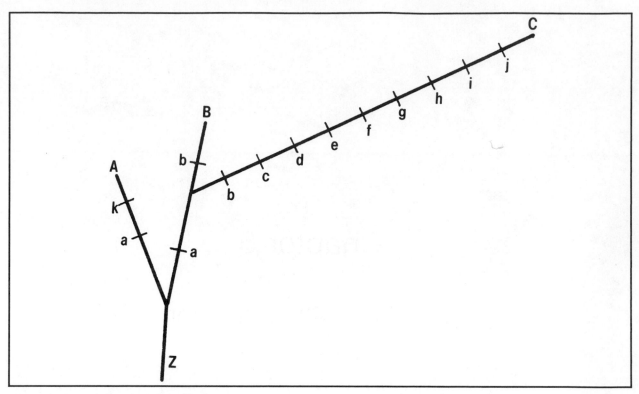

Figure 5.1 Cladogram of hypothetical taxa A, B, and C (modified from Mayr, 1981)

While most of the rules and conventions of biological classification are well established, there remain many conflicts and disagreements among the classifiers. Even the species concept, which is the basis of Linnaean classification system, is debated. Most biologists today agree to the following definition of species: "species are groups of actually or potentially interbreeding natural populations, which are reproductively isolated from other such groups." (Mayr, 1970:120). Unfortunately, one of the primary criteria of this definition, the potential to interbreed, is often impossible to determine in natural populations. Futhermore, there are many degrees of interbreeding potential among natural populations: some animals may be able to interbreed but their offspring are infertile; or the fertility of offspring may be slightly less than the offspring of "true species." In practice most species determinations are made on the basis of morphological similarity or dissimilarity. Classifiers often disagree, however, on what morphological criteria should be used in their classifications. For example, should the shape of the skull, the morphology of the teeth, the color of the coats or biomolecular data be weighted more, less, or equally in making species designations?

Disagreements arise in making classifications above the species level as well. Most biologists (by no means all) believe the higher taxonomic categories of organisms should be determined on the basis of the organism's evolutionary history: organisms which are more closely related should be placed in the same taxa while those more distantly related should be placed in different taxa. The phylogenetic approach to classification is divided into two schools: cladistics and **evolutionary classification** (Mayr 1981). Cladistic classification (cladism) is based exclusively on geneology. That is, a genus should include a group of species all descended from the same common ancestor; a

```
Order:  Primates

    Suborder:  Prosimii

        Superfamily:  Lorisoidea (loris, bushbaby, potto)
        Superfamily:  Lemuroidea (lemurs of Madagascar)
        Superfamily:  Tarsiioidea (tarsier)

    Suborder:  Anthropoidea (higher primates:  monkeys, apes and humans)

      Infraorder:  Platyrrhini (New World monkeys)

        Superfamily:  Ceboidea

          Family:  Callitrichidae (Tamarins and marmosets)
          Family:  Cebidae (squirrel monkey, spider monkey, capuchin
                           monkey, howler monkey and others.)

      Infraorder:  Catarrhini (Old World monkeys, apes and humans)

        Superfamily:  Cercopithecoidea (Old World monkeys)

          Family:  Cercopithecidae (baboons, macaques, mangabeys,
                             guenons, and others)
          Family:  Colobidae (langurs and other colobine monkeys)

        Superfamily:  Hominoidea (apes and humans)

          Family:  Hylobatidae (lesser ages, gibbons and siamang)
          Family:  Pongidae  (Great apes, chimpanzees, gorilla, and
                           Orang-utan)
          Family:  Hominidae (humans)
```

Figure 5.2 A Traditional Primate Classification

family should include a group of genera all descended from the same common
ancestor, and so on. On the other hand, while evolutionary classification is
the same as cladism in that it is based on evolutionary history, it also takes
into account different rates of evolution in different lineages (see Mayr,
1981 for discussion). In Figure 5.1, cladists would combine A and C into one
taxon because they shared a common ancestor: Z. Evolutionary taxonomists, on
the other hand, would put A and C into separate taxa because C has many
derived characters (b through j) not shared with A.

PRIMATE CLASSIFICATION

Two primate classification systems are presented in this chapter: a traditional (Figure 5.2) and a more recent (Figure 5.3) system. The two major
differences in the two primate classification schemes concern the relationship
of the tarsier to higher primates and that of great apes to humans.

```
Order:  Primates                              [common name if different from above]

    Suborder:  Strepsirhini

        Superfamily:  Lemuroidea
        Superfamily:  Lorisoidea

    Suborder:  Haplorhini

      Infraorder:  Tarsii

        Superfamily:  Tarsiodidea

          Family:  Tarsiidae              [the tarsier]

      Infraorder:  Platyrrhini

        Superfamily:  Ceboidea

          Family:  Callimiconidae         [Goeldis marmoset]
          Family:  Callitrichidae         [other marmosets and tamarins]
          Family:  Ceboidea

      Infraorder:  Catarrhini

        Superfamily:  Cercopithecoidea

          Family:  Cercopithecidae

            Subfamily:  Cercopithecinae
            Subfamily:  Colobinae

        Superfamily:  Hominoidea

          Family:  Hylobatidae
          Family:  Pongidae               [the orang-utan]
          Family:  Hominidae

            Subfamily:  Gorillinae        [Gorilla and Chimpanzee]

            Subfamily:  Homininae         [Humans]
```

Figure 5.3 Classification of Primates (modified from Richard, 1985)

Tarsiers today live only on island areas of Southeast Asia. They share a number of characteristics with other prosimians (lemurs and lorises), includ-ing a primitive dental pattern and social behavior, small bodies and large ears. However, tarsiers also show many similarities to the higher primates. Their eye orbits are completely enclosed by bone (unlike other prosim-ians); they possess a bony ear canal more like that of anthropoids; and they lack a rhinarium (a wet, naked portion that surrounds the nostrils, possessed by all other non-anthropoid land-living mammals). Furthermore, the tarsiers have an anthropoid placentation form, and biomolecular data show the tarsiers to be more closely related to anthropoids than to other prosimians (Dene, et al. 1976). Therefore, tarsiers are classified in the suborder Haplorhini in Figure 5.3, while the other prosimians are classified in the suborder Strep-sirhini.

In addition, comparative morphology, and comparative biomolecular and fossil data, strongly suggest that African apes shared a common ancestor with humans after both taxa had shared a common ancestor with the Asian great ape, the orang-utan. Therefore the more recent primate classification system (Figure 5.3) lumps the African apes and humans in the same family (Hominidae) separate from the family which contains the orang-utan (Pongidae). The African apes and humans are then separated from each other at the subfamily level in this classification scheme.

Exercises

1. List the endings for these categories in biological taxa.

        suffix for superfamily   _____

        suffix for family   _____

        suffix for subfamily   _____

2. List the differences in the two primate classifications systems   (Figures
    5.2 and 5.3).

3. Is the more traditional (Figure 5.2) primate scheme from the cladistic or
    evolutionary classification school? Why?

4. Is the more recent (Figure 5.3) primate scheme from the cladistic or
    evoltuionary classification school? Why?

Chapter 6

Comparison of the Skeletons of
Quadrupeds, Bipeds, and Brachiators

INTRODUCTION

First, familiarize yourself with some of the tools used in the physical anthropology laboratory: sliding calipers, spreading calipers, osteometric board
(bone board) and the Mollison's Craniophore (see Figures 6.1, 6.2, and 6.3).
Be sure you know how to use each of these instruments, as you will use them
to demonstrate the differences between the skeletons of quadrupeds, brachiators, and bipeds. Please note however, that the term "brachiator" can only be
accurately applied to gibbons and siamangs, and the "typical biped" is, of
course, Homo sapiens.

It is important to understand the basic differences between living quadrupeds
and bipeds (humans) so that we may interpret the fossils we find. If you
found a skeleton of a cow in a cornfield, for instance, you know that the bony
structures are inappropriate for a human skeleton. But what if you found only
a fragment of that cow skeleton? Would you still be able to recognize the
clues? In this chapter you will learn some of the many clues used by paleoanthropologists. All of these characteristics vary greatly in each group, and
so are given here only for general comparative purposes. The following is a
compilation of data from Schultz 1937, 1973; Le Gros Clark 1959; and Campbell
1976, 1985.

	Typical Quadruped	Typical Biped	Typical Brachiator
Shape of the vertebral column	Single curve from neck neck to pelvis: similar to cantilever bridge	"S"-shaped curve	Single gentle curve from neck to pelvis
Shape of vertebral bodies	Cylindrical, relatively regular in shape from neck to pelvis	More wedge-shaped, differences in shape between neck and pelvis greater than in quadrupeds	Intermediate
Size of vertebral bodies	Similar in size from neck to pelvis	Great differences in size between neck and pelvis	Intermediate
Size of spinous processes* (see note on page 89)	Huge, especially those at the origin of nuchal (neck) muscles	Small, as the large area for the origin of "nuchal" muscles is not needed: cranium is more balanced over the vertebral column	Fairly small
Center of gravity of animal body	Over the forelimbs: the forelimbs catch the body in locomotion and aid in propulsion	Closer to the hind-limbs: propulsion through the hind-limbs	Intermediate
Shape of Thorax	Narrow, deep thorax, narrow sternum	Shallow, broad thorax, wide sternum, perhaps as a result of arm-swinging ancestors	Shallow, broad thorax, wide sternum
Tail	Occurs in some quadrupeds, not in apes	Caudal vertebrae curved ventrally, aid in support of viscera	No tail
Number of Lumbar Vertebrae	Varies: monkeys usually 9: great flexibility in spinal column	5 to 6: little flexibility, greater stability	6: flexibility of quadrupedal monkeys mostly lost

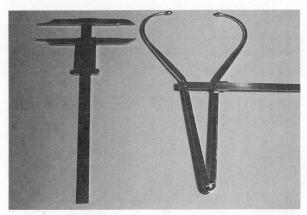

Figure 6.1 Sliding Calipers (left)
        Spreading Calipers (right)

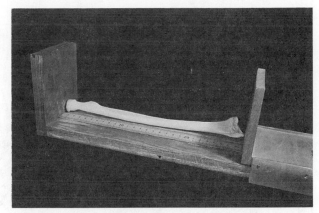

Figure 6.2 Osteometric Board

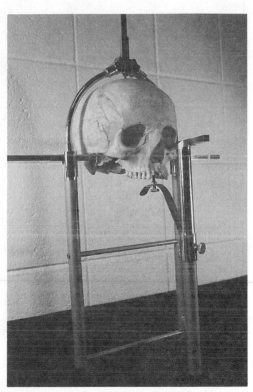

Figure 6.3 Mollison's
        Craniophore

*Cervical vertebra spinous processes are proportional to weight carried by the "nuchal" muscles. The spinous processes in some quadrupedal monkeys are short, allowing increased range of motion in spinal column.

These evolutionary differences have created some problems for the biped, in that the wedge-shaped vertebral bodies and the "S"-shaped curve result in less stability in the back. The nucleus pulposus, the fluid of toothpaste consistency inside the intervertebral disks (the cushions between the vertebrae), will be extruded beyond its normal limits with very little downward force, often exerting pressure on a spinal nerve root and causing pain. In addition to back pain, the ligaments holding the gut of the quadrupeds originate from the spinal column and hang ventrally, and the weight of the intestinal contents is evenly distributed through these ligaments. The same ligaments are present in humans, but gravity is pulling the intestinal contents caudally instead of ventrally, making them more difficult to support, and increasing the likelihood of herniation of the abdominal wall.

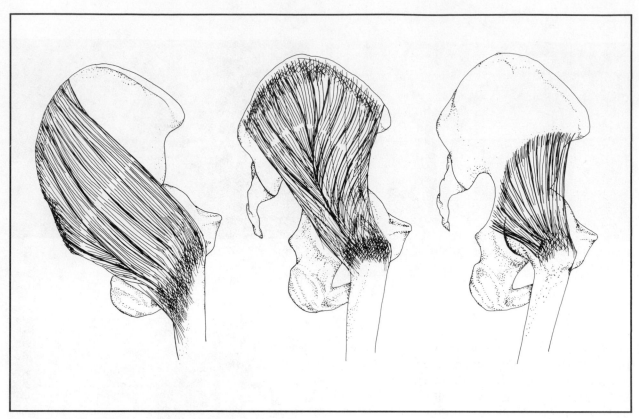

Figure 6.4 Biped Gluteus Muscles:
  Gluteus Maximus (left), Gluteus Medius (middle), Gluteus Minimus (right)

The Pelvis

	Typical Quadruped	Typical Biped	Typical Brachiator
Ilium	Long and narrow, Greater Sciatic Notch is very shallow, forming an obtuse angle	Short and splayed, Greater Sciatic Notch is deeper, less obtuse	Intermediate
Gluteus Muscles	Gluteus maximus, medius, and minimus are all abductors (draws leg away from midline of body)	Gluteus maximus is an extensor (see Figure 6.1)	

Because of the changes in the ilium, the center of gravity is different in the pelvic region between quadrupeds and bipeds. The area of articulation of the sacrum and ilium (the auricular surface, because it looks like an ear) in humans has moved with the ilium until it is closer to the acetabulum, which brings the weight from the spinal column closer to the femur head. This is a more stable arrangement for a biped. Abductors and adductors of the femur maintain lateral balance by shifting body weight more over the sagittal line (midline) of the body. The lateral extension of the ilium and the lengthening of the femoral neck adds power by increasing the lever arm for these muscles.

The Limbs

	Typical Quadruped	Typical Biped	Typical Brachiator
Intermembral Index (to be measured: formula given later)	In typical primitive mammals, the forelimbs and hindlimbs are of equal length; notable variations in primates	Hindlimbs are longer than forelimbs	Forelimbs longer than hindlimbs
Tibia and Fibula	Many primitive mammals use both bones for rotary movement of the foot: the tibia transmits weight, the fibula allows rotation** (see pg. 76)	Humans have lost most lateral rotation of foot afforded by the fibula	Retention of rotary movement of foot
Foot	Highly variable; differences between monkeys and apes noted later	Transmits weight through triad: heel, outside of foot, then roll off of great toe	Retention of grasping ability

**In some quadrupeds such as the bison and horse, the fibula and ulna are both very greatly reduced.

There are three distinct functions of the forelimbs in most mammals: they support the body in a quadruped; suspend the body in brachiators; and they manipulate objects in bipeds.

Miscellaneous

	Typical Quadruped	Typical Biped	Typical Brachiator
Scapula	Located on the side of the body, the glenoid fossa is more nearly in line with the lateral line of the scapula; points downward	Located on dorsum of body, glenoid fossa more open, allowing wider movement of arm	Located on dorsum, glenoid fossa fairly open, points more cranially than in humans
Clavicle	Is absent in typical quadrupedal mammal, is very little lateral movement of forelimbs	Is present, allows stable lateral motion of the humerus	Is present, even longer than in humans
Hands	The form of the hands varies from one finger present as in the horse, to five fingers in monkeys and humans. The specific characteristics of brachiators, quadrupedal monkeys, apes, and humans will be discussed later.		Hands hooklike with very long curved fingers and reduced thumb

Prognathism (projection of lower face)	Extensive prognathism, very long tooth row, very long snout	Reduced prognathism, short tooth row, nasal area and tooth row more directly under forehead	More similar to biped than to quadruped
Foramen Magnum	Near rear of cranium	More centrally located under cranium: cranium almost balanced on spinal column	Intermediate

The above features of the skull explain the difference in the area of the occipital region of the cranium devoted to the origin of nuchal muscles (See page 4 for discussion of "nuchal muscles"). The quadruped cranium and mandible extend very far beyond the foramen magnum and the muscle mass needed to counteract the forces of gravity on the snout is very much greater than that needed to hold up the biped cranium, which is almost perfectly balanced on the spine.

Therefore:

	Typical Quadruped	Typical Biped	Typical Brachiator
Nuchal Crest (area for origin of nuchal muscles on occiput	Very large, rough area indicating origin of substantial nuchal muscles	No nuchal crest, merely a slightly roughened area on the occiput, often difficult to see	Similar to biped
Mastoid Process insertion of Sterno-Cleido-Mastoid Muscle)	Very small, as there is little need to bring the cranium from a dorsal to a ventral position with a muscle when gravity will function as well	Fairly large, as now the cranium is more balanced on spinal column, and if skull is tilted dorsally, these muscles may bring it to upright position	Not pronounced

In order for a very large muscle to function, it needs a very large area of origin so as to anchor itself against the forces needed to perform its task. As a muscle becomes larger, it spreads out over the bone of its origin, until it becomes so large that it literally runs out of bone on which to anchor itself. The bone is then stimulated (through the piezoelectric effect) to produce more bone in order to provide this attachment area (a muscle cannot anchor itself to another muscle) and will produce the crests you see in the occipital and sagittal regions of the gorilla cranium. Note the following drawings:

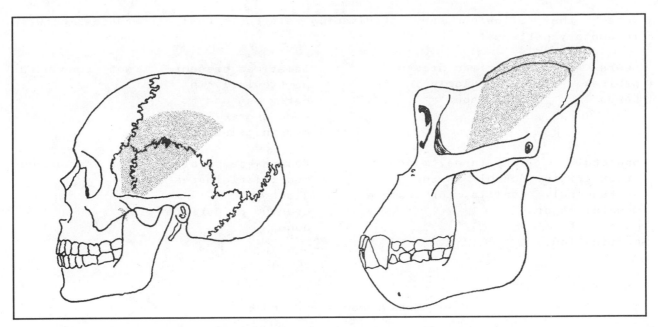

Figure 6.5 Origin of Temporal Muscle in Modern Humans and Gorilla
   Not drawn to scale

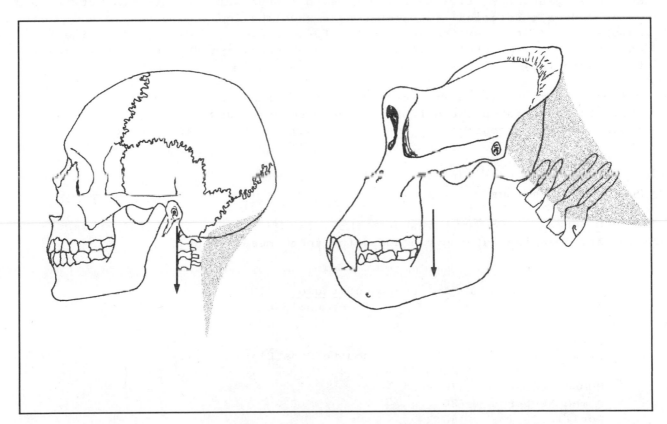

Figure 6.6 Origin of "Nuchal Muscles" in Modern Humans and Gorilla
   The arrows represent the center of gravity.   Not drawn to scale

Note: the following are <u>not</u> directly related to the differences between locomotory patterns!

Supra-orbital torus	Sometimes present, particularly in the great apes	Sometimes present particularly in early man and to some degree in modern males	Not pronounced
Sagittal Crest origin of temporal muscle: major muscle of mastication)	Very large, most notable in the gorilla, for example	Absent--temporal muscle originates along side of cranium on parietal bones	Not pronounced

Measurements and Indices

An index is the ratio of one measurement to another, expressed as a percentage. Indices have been used for decades in anthropometry both in the living and dead, and are still used today even though multivariate statistics and other modern statistical techniques have made the index obsolete in some circumstances. An index is very useful for quick, preliminary investigations, and is also very useful in describing evolutionary trends and general population variation.

Below is an abbreviated list of indices and measurements. You will use some of them in describing the differences between quadrupeds and bipeds, and in evolutionary comparisons. Keep your results on the chart provided.

Postcranial Indices:

A. <u>Brachial Index</u>: measures the relative lengths of the upper and lower arm (use the osteometric board for these measurements)

$$\frac{\text{Length of radius} \times 100}{\text{Length of humerus}}$$

Average values (Schultz 1937 and Le Gros Clark 1959):

Human Groups	76
Human Newborns	80
Gorillas	80
Chimpanzees	93
Orang-utans	100
Gibbons	113

B.   Crural Index: measures the relative lengths of the upper and lower leg
      bones (use the osteometric board for these measurements).

                    Bicondylar Length of Tibia X 100
                      Bicondylar Length of Femur

Note: The Bicondylar Length of the Tibia measures from the flat surface
of the lateral condyle to the distal tip of the medial malleolus, and
does not include the intercondyloid eminence.

The Bicondylar Length of the Femur is measured by placing both condyles
on one flat end of the bone board and bringing the moveable end into
contact with the head.

Average Values (Schultz 1937):

Human Groups   83 - 89
Gorillas   80
Chimpanzees   83
Gibbons   87
Orang-utan   92

C.   Intermembral Index: measures the relative lengths of the upper and lower
      limbs

                    Length of humerus + radius   X 100
                    Bicondylar lengths of femur + tibia

Average Values (Schultz 1937, Le Gros Clark 1959)

Human Groups   64 - 79   Alway while
Human Newborns   104
Chimpanzees   107   ①   ②   ③   ④
Gorillas   117
Gibbons   178   Orang-utan Chimpanzee Gorila human
Orang-utans   144

Cranial Indices

A.   Cranial Index: measures the shape of the cranium (see measurement ins-
      tructions below)

                      Cranial Breadth X 100
                        Cranial Length

(Martin and Saller 1957, Bass 1987):

Dolicocrany   up to 74.9   (narrow or long-headed)
Mesocrany   75.0 to 79.9 (average)
Brachycrany   80.0 to 84.9 (round-headed)
Hyperbrachycrany   85.0 and up (even more rounded)

B.   Nasal Index: measures the shape of the nasal (bony) aperture (see measurement instructions below)

$$\frac{\text{Nasal Breadth}}{\text{Nasal Height}} \times 100$$

(Martin and Saller 1957, Bass 1987):

Leptorrhiny   up to 47.9   (narrow aperture)
Mesorrhiny   48.0 to 52.9 (average or medium)
Platyrrhiny   53.0 and up (broad aperture)

The numerical values of indices C, D, and E increase as one moves "up" the evolutionary scale toward humans.

C.   Condylar Index: measures the position of the foramen magnum
     (see landmark diagram)

$$\frac{\text{Basion to Opisthocranion}}{\text{Basion to Prosthion}} \times 100$$

D.   Palatal Index: measures the shape of the palate (and hence of the mouth and lower face).

$$\frac{\text{Palatal Width}}{\text{Palatal Length}} \times 100$$

E.   Supraorbital Index: measures the height of the skull.

$$\frac{\text{Vertex to Superior Border of Eye}}{\text{Vertex to Inferior Border of Eye}} \times 100$$

F.   Nuchal Index: measures the area given for origin of nuchal muscles. This index decreases as one moves "up" the evolutionary scale toward humans.

$$\frac{\text{From Line Level With Inferior Border of Eye to Line with Inion}}{\text{From Vertex to Line with Inferior Border of Eye}} \times 100$$

Skull Volume

     Volumetric Method: to be used on complete, intact skulls
     a. Plug holes and openings with cotton (except the foramen magnum)
     b. Fill cranium through the foramen magnum with suitable material:
         (mustard seed or millet are very good)
     c. Gently shake the skull to settle the seed.
     d. When filled to the border of the foramen magnum, carefully empty the
         seed into a large volumetric cylinder. Record the volume.

Measurement Instructions

Note: cranial measurements are to be taken while the skull is in the Frank-furt Plane, which is a standard plane of reference used worldwide. The cranium is placed in the Mollison's Craniophore, or in a position in which the lower border of the eye and porion are in the same horizontal plane.

Cranial Length:	From glabella to opisthocranion
Cranial Breadth:	Maximum transverse diameter
Nasal Breadth:	Maximum breadth of nasal cavity
Nasal Height:	From nasion to nasospinale
Palatal Length:	From just behind the point of prosthion to end of palate
Palatal Width:	From the insides of the second molars

Cranial Landmarks (Bass 1987):

Basion: The midpoint of the anterior margin of the foramen magnum most distant from the bregma.

Glabella: The most forward projecting point in the midline of the forehead at the level of the supra-orbital ridges and above the nasofrontal suture [the suture which separates the frontal and nasal bones], (Figure 6.7a)

Inion: A point at the base of the external occipital protuberance. It is the intersection of the mid-sagittal plane with a line drawn tangent to the uppermost convexity of the right and left superior nuchal line (Figure 6.7b).

Nasion: Intersection of the nasofrontal suture with the midsagittal plane (Figure 6.7c).

Nasospinale: The point where a line drawn between the lower margins of the right and left nasal apertures is intersected by the midsagittal plane) (Figure 6.7d).

Opisthocranion: The most posterior point on the skull not on the external occipital protuberance.

Prosthion: The most anterior point in the midline on the upper alveolar process (Figure 6.7e).

Vertex: The highest point in the midsagittal contour [when the cranium is in the Frankfort plane] (Figure 6.7f).

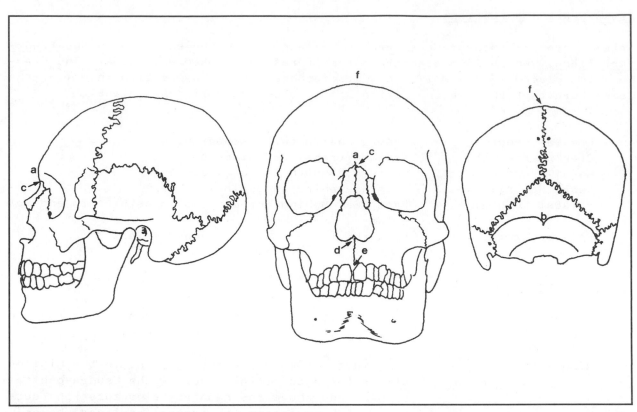

Figure 6.7   Landmarks of the Skull

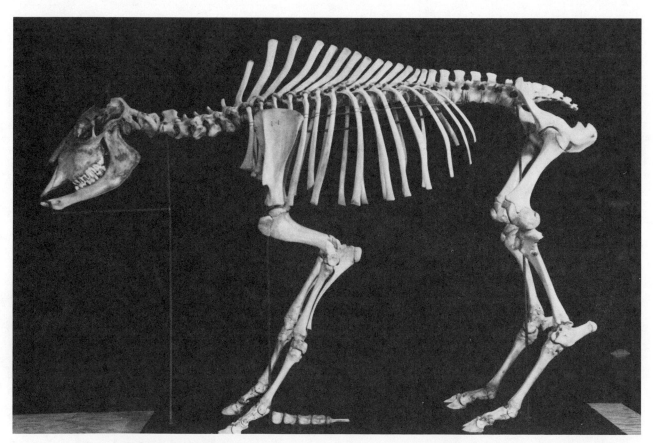

Figure 6.8:   Adolescent Bison

Problems

1. What is the intermembral index of the bison in Figure 6.8?

    The brachial index?

    The crural index?

2. If you found a fossil with a very large sagittal crest, what would that
    feature indicate about the animal's masticatory apparatus relative to its
    cranial size?

3. If you found a fossil which had a very large nuchal crest, what would you
    expect of the size of the spinous processes of the thoracic vertebrae?

4. If a fossil had very long hook-like fingers with a short thumb, what would
    this probably indicate about its locomotor ancestry?

Chapter 7

Comparing the Living Primates

We have made very general comparisons of the anatomies of quadrupedal and bi-pedal animals (Chapter 6), and now we will take a closer look at the anatomi-cal differences and similarities of a few of the major groups of primates, which will not only allow a better understanding of the living primates, but will prepare us to understand and interpret the fossil record. The discussions and exercises will refer to skeletons of prosimians, New World monkeys, Old World monkeys, apes and humans, so if these skeletons are not available in your laboratory, observe and study the photographs and the drawings provided here. We will first study the general characteristics common to all primates, then the postcrania to correlate certain characteristics with their primary locomotor modes. We will then compare dentition of the major groups of living primates, as the dentition is the most often discovered fossilized material.

Note the differences between "primitive" and "derived" characteristics. Primitive characteristics are those that are common to many groups of primates (and sometimes even primitive mammals), and so are closer to an evolutionary divergence, while derived (or specialized) traits are common to few primates, and are probably evolved for a special function (e.g. the human foot).

101

PRIMATE CHARACTERISTICS

1. Retention of five digits on hands and feet
2. Nails on all digits

    A claw is retained on at least one digit in some of the lower primates, and is used for grooming.
3. Primate hands and feet are usually prehensile: that is, they are adapted for grasping

    Man is the only living primate with a true "opposable thumb", that is, the tip of the thumb can be touched to the tips of all other fingers.
4. Reduction of the importance of the sense of smell. Primates usually have shorter snouts
5. An increase in the importance of vision: primate eyes are usually close together at the front of the face, allowing good binocular vision which enhances depth perception. Most higher primates also possess good color vision.

    In most primates the eye orbit is completely enclosed by bone, thereby increasing the protection of the eye. Prosimians are the exception to this rule: tarsiers are the only prosimians with completely enclosed eye orbits.
6. Primates usually only have one infant at a time. Twins are rare, except in the New World Monkey family, the Callithricidae (tamarins and marmosets), where twins are the rule.
7. An increase in the time of infant dependency: primate infants are born in a more helpless and dependent condition and for a longer period of time relative to most other mammals. There is therefore an increased learning and socialization period.
8. Primates usually have large brains relative to their body size.
9. Primates usually live in social groups consisting of both sexes and all age-grades (adults, juveniles, and infants). This type of sociality is not common in other orders of mammals.

POSTCRANIAL COMPARISONS AND LOCOMOTION

We will discuss 6 modes of primate locomotion:

1. Slow quadrupedal climbing (SQC): prosimians
2. Vertical clinging and leaping (VCL): prosimians
3. Quadupedal walking, running, leaping: monkeys
4. Brachiation: gibbons and siamangs
5. Knuckle walking: a sub-category of quadrupedalism found in African apes, chimpanzees and gorillas
6. Bipedalism: humans

Primates exhibit much variety and versatility in their locomotor behavior especially in the trees where most of them spend all or part of their existence. By simply stating that a primate is a quadruped or a brachiator, for example, hardly describes all the movements a primate must make in order to earn a living in their natural habitats. Siamangs, for example, while generally classified as brachiators (using the forearms to swing beneath branches) tend to move primarily by climbing when feeding (Fleagle 1976) and may sometimes move bipedally on top of branches.

102

Slow quadrupedal climbing

This specialized mode of locomotion is seen only in the pottos of Africa and lorises of South Asia. Unlike all others, these primates, never run or leap in their arboreal habitat, but always move very slowly and deliberately. These prosimians are nocturnal, and their slow, quiet mode of locomotion allows them to stalk prey (insects, birds and lizards) and to avoid predators in the trees. Slow quadrupedal climbers are characterized by robust musculature and limb bones, mobile ankle, wrist and hip joints, and short or absent tails (Figure 7.1). If your laboratory has a loris or potto skeleton, fill in one of the blank columns of the chart on page 111.

Vertical clinging and leaping

The bushbaby (Galago sp.) of Africa (Figure 7.2) and other prosimians of similar anatomical structure exhibit a locomotor mode which has been called "vertical clinging and leaping" (VCL). Prosimians which typically move in this way push off with their powerful hind limbs from a vertical or near-vertical support to which they were clinging, turn around while in mid-air, then land feet first on another branch or tree trunk (Figure 7.3). Compare the relative lengths of the fore-limbs and hindlimbs of the bushbaby by determining its intermembral index (page 95). Fill in the chart on page 111.

Monkey quadrupedalism

Most monkeys are quadrupeds and those which are primarily arboreal (a majority of them) can be called "quadrupedal runners and leapers". That is, they move on top of the branches quadrupedally and leap

Figure 7.1 Asian Loris

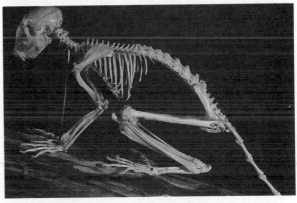

Figure 7.2 Bushbaby (Galago sp.)

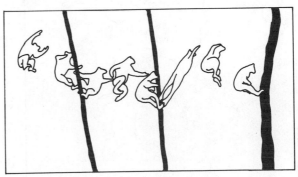

Figure 7.3 Vertical Clinging and Leaping (courtesy, A. Walker)

103

Figure 7.4 Quadrupedal Running

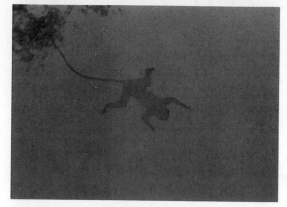

Figure 7.5 Leaping Monkey

from tree to tree when there is a break in the forest canopy by using their strong hind limbs to propel themselves, and using their tails as "rudders" (see Figures 7.4 and 7.5). There are subtle differences between the skeletons of terrestrial Old World monkeys (e.g. baboons) and and those that are completely arboreal but they will not be mentioned here. The Old World monkeys are adept at moving their limbs in a relatively limited plane, and they rarely suspend themselves beneath a branch by hanging from their forelimbs.

There are many similarities between the New World and Old World Monkeys thought to be a result of parallel evolution. These are adaptations to a similar way of life in similar habitats, in this case in the canopy of tropical rainforests. There are a few differences, however, between the two groups. Some of the New World Monkeys (but no Old World Monkeys) have prehensile tails, used as a "5th hand" in manipulating objects or hanging from branches. Ground-living behavior is rare among New World Monkeys, but is more common in the Old World Monkeys.

Figure 7.6 Brachiation

Small ape brachiation

The small apes, (gibbons and siamangs of Southeast Asia) habitually swing, or brachiate, beneath the branches (Figure 7.6), and sometimes feed while hanging by their forelimbs. This activity is aided by the position of their scapulae, by the upward orientation of their glenoid cavities, and by their hook-like hands with small thumbs and long fingers. When climbing in the trees, they use their forelimbs and strong upper bodies much more than their legs. In short, the locomotion and posture habits of the small apes can be said to be forelimb and upper-body dominated (Fleagle 1976).

African ape knuckle-walking

Though the great apes share most of the morphological characteristics of the small apes
and occasionally brachiate for short distances, they are too large to habitually
brachiate through the forest canopy. African
apes (chimpanzees and gorillas) carry out
most long distance movements on the ground by
"knuckle-walking". The knuckle-walkers, (Figure 7.7) are characterized by tough, hairless
skin on the dorsum of the middle fingers,
and their wrists are strengthened by differences in the carpals. When these apes climb
trees, however, they, like the lesser apes,
use their forearms and strong upper bodies
more than their hind limbs, and often use a
variety of hanging or suspensory postures.

Figure 7.7 Knuckle
Walking, Male Gorilla

Humans:

The locomotor habits of humans are well
known. Anatomists have long recognized the
similarities between humans and apes in the
upper body: the position of the scapula on
the dorsum of the thorax, the triangular
shape of the scapula, the relative antero-
posterior shallowness of the thorax, and the
upward orientation of the glenoid cavity.
(Figure 7.8). These are similarities not
necessarily due to current similarities in
locomotory behaviour, however, but are due to
the long period of evolutionary relatedness.

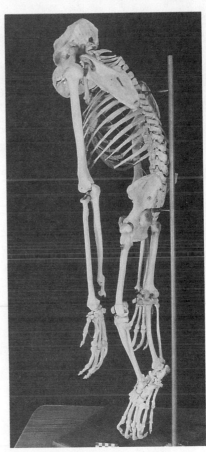

Figure 7.8 Orang-utan
Lateral View

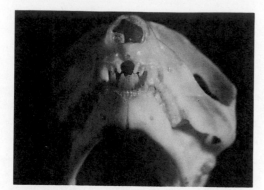

Figure 7.9 Bushbaby Tooth Comb

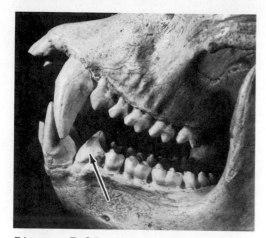

Figure 7.10 Sectorial Lower
First Premolar

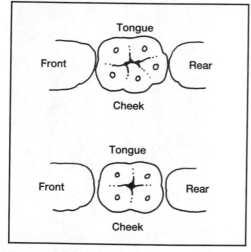

Figure 7.11 Y-5 Molar (top)
Bilophodont Molar (bottom)

Incisors:

Most primitive mammals have 4 incisors in
each quadrant, while most primates have 2.

Most living primates have at least somewhat procumbent (forward-projecting) incisors, but incisors generally became more
vertically oriented through hominid evolution.

Note the mandibular incisors (Figure 7.9)
of the bushbaby (Galago sp.). This is a
"tooth comb", and is used by many prosimians to groom its own fur or the fur of
another member of the social group.

Canines:

The small canines are perhaps the most
distinguishing features of human teeth.
Through hominid evolution the canines have
become more incisor-like, and extend only
very little beyond the tooth line. The
canine is, however, used as a tool for
defense and gripping in many primates (the
gorilla, chimpanzee and baboon are good
examples).

Note the diastema (the gap which receives
the canine of the opposite jaw), especially in those animals with very large canines, as in baboons and gorillas (Figure
7.10).

Premolars:

Very primitive mammals had 4 premolars.
The first premolar in the tooth row was
lost first to give the New World Monkey
formula: 2:1:3:3. The second premolar in
the tooth row was lost next to give the
dental formula of Old World Monkeys, Apes
and Man: 2:1:2:3. The practice by paleontologists is, therefore, to state that our
dental formula includes premolars 3 and 4.

Modern pongids and some monkeys have a
sectorial lower first premolar, (P_3), a
single-cusped premolar which forms a cutting, slicing complex with the cutting
edge of the upper canine (Figure 7.10).
Note that the upper canine of these forms

is honed by the sectorial premolar. Later in human evolution this sectorial lower premolar adds a cusp to become a true "bicuspid".

All premolars become more molar-like in hominid evolution, that is, they become wider, with a more effective grinding surface.

Molars:

Old World Monkeys have bilophodont molars, which usually have four cusps situated in two parallel rows (sometimes a 5th cusp is also present). Y-5 (or 5-Y) molars have 5 cusps which look like a "Y", and are located in the mandibles of most apes and humans (Figure 7.11). Only hominoids (apes and humans) among living primates have Y-5 molars.

The trend through hominid evolution is for the molars to become less linear (from the front of the mouth to the rear), as in the vegetarian New World Monkey, and to become more square. Through early hominid evolution, the enamel has become thicker on the molars.

Tooth Row Shape:

Very early primates have tooth rows that are divergent toward the back. Through hominid evolution the shape of the tooth row has changed from those like the modern gorilla (rectangular, long tooth row), to a parabolic shape as in modern man (Figure 7.12). As a coincident change with this difference in tooth row form, the entire face has become less prognathic (in which the lower part of the face protrudes forward). The snout has become generally smaller and the face set more under the cranial vault. Through hominid evolution, then, the parabola of the tooth row has become wider.

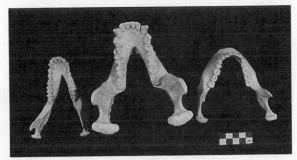

Figure 7.12 Tooth Row Shape
Old World Monkey (left)
Gorilla (center)
Human (right)

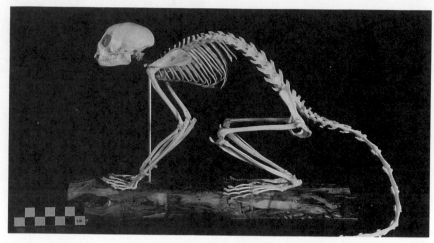

Figure 7.13 New World Monkey (Squirrel Monkey)

dental formula: 2133

Figure 7.14 Old World Monkey (Macaque)

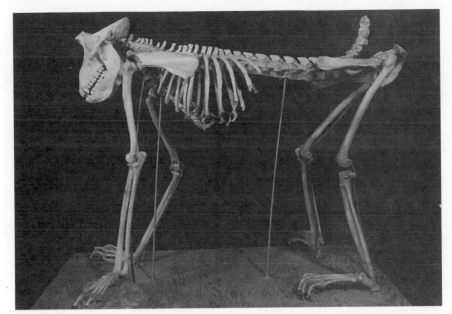

Figure 7.15 Old World Monkey (Female Common Baboon, top of cranium missing)

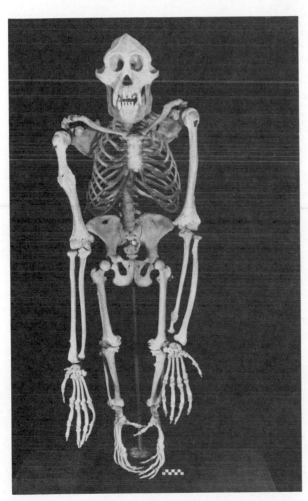

Figure 7.16 Ape (Orang-utan)

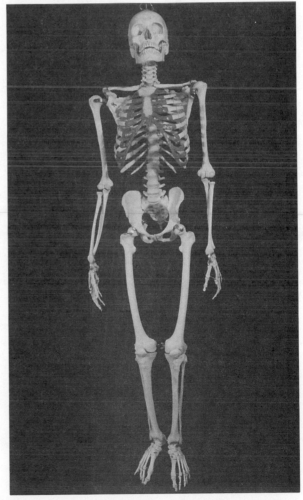

Figure 7.17 Human

Fill out the charts for the Prosimians (Figure 7.2), New World Monkey (Figure 7.13), an Old World Monkey (Figures 7.14, 7.15), Ape (Figures 7.8, 7.16), and Human (Figure 7.17).

COMPARISONS OF EXTANT PRIMATES

Specify:	Prosimian	New World Cebid	Old World Monkey	Ape	Human
Intermembral Index					
Condylar Index					
Dental Formula					
Enclosed Eye Orbits?					
Location of Scapula on Thorax					
Nails On All Digits					
Tail?					

Chapter 8

Observation of Living Primate Behavior and Morphology

INTRODUCTION

This chapter involves an exercise in observing behavior and morphology of zoo primates. Before visiting the zoo, review the typical locomotor behavior and other physical characteristics and classification of major groups of primates discussed in previous chapters.

Naturally, the primate morphology is not greatly different between the zoo and the wild, but the behavior of primates in zoos can be atypical. Studies of baboons in a very crowded enclosure in a London zoo in the 1930s gave the impression that primate societies were centered around sex and violence. Studies of primates in their natural habitats which began in earnest in the 1950s and 1960s have shown that, while sex and violence are certainly parts of the behavioral repertoire of primates, they are exhibited rarely relative to other aspects of their behavior, such as foraging for food, grooming behavior, and mother-infant relationships.

The locomotor behavior of primates in zoos obviously depends to a large extent on what they have available in their cages and enclosures. An arboreal primate will not be able to exhibit its full repertoire of arboreal agility, for example, if its cage consists only of bars and a concrete floor.

Also note that many of the behaviors listed below will be season-specific, and will be determined to some extent by the number, ages, and sexes of individual present within each enclosure.

The zoo personnel will often provide some of the information needed to complete the checklist, such as the species and common names and their distributions.

Behavioral Categories

There are basically two methods for observing primates: either specific behavioral categories are chosen, or all of the behavior of a specific (focal) animal or group of animals is observed and behavior recorded. If, for example, a female in the zoo has recently given birth, the researcher may wish to concentrate on mother-infant interactions. If, on the other hand, a group of primates includes many juveniles, research may focus on play behavior. Below is a short list of behavior categories to chose from:

1. Mother-infant interactions
2. Play behavior
3. Sexual behavior-mounting behavior
4. Adult male-adult female interactions
5. Adult male-juvenile interations
6. Adult male-adult male interactions
7. Adult female-adult female interactions
8. Adult female-juvenile interactions
9. Agonistic behavior
10. Dominance behavior

In order to fully understand the behavior sequences observed, one must usually be familiar with the individual and group histories. For example, an adult female may interact with an adult female to which she is closely related quite differently than to one to which she is not related. Because of this, we recommend that the student chose a focal animal or focal group of animals and record whatever behavior they exhibit over a given time period.

Sampling Techniques

There are many sampling techniques used to record primate behavior. Below is a brief summary of some of the more common techniques.

1. Scan Sampling: The researcher records the behavior of a group of primates or an individual at regular time intervals, usually 30 seconds, 1 minute, or 5 minutes. Obviously, if one wishes to use this method with a group of primates, the group should not be too large, and all members should be visible at all times.

2. Ad-Lib Sampling: The researcher records any behavior of a group of primates that are observable and which seems interesting. Recordings are made on a blank sheet of paper or a field notebook. While regular time intervals are not used in ad-lib sampling, the time should be recorded often. Also, the researcher usually develops a form of abbreviations since this method involves much writing.

Part of the class might employ the scan sampling-focal animal technique, and the rest use the ad-lib technique on the same group over the same time period. A comparison of what was observed should be made in the laboratory, and the advantages and disadvantages of each method discussed.

CLASSIFICATION, MORPHOLOGY
AND LOCOMOTION

Date_____ Name_____Section_____

Common name_____ Common name_____

Infraorder_____ Infraorder_____

Superfamily_____ Superfamily_____

Family_____ Family_____

Subfamily_____ Subfamily_____

Genus_____ Genus_____

Species_____ Species_____

Distribution_____ Distribution_____

Tail?_____ Tail?_____

Prehensile tail?_____ Prehensile tail?_____

Nails on all digits?_____ Nails on all digits?_____

Relative length of forelimbs to   Relative length of forelimbs to
   hindlimbs_____   hindlimbs_____

Habitual mode of locomotion   Habitual mode of locomotion
_____   _____

Sexual dimorphism in body size_____ Sexual dimorphism in body size_____

ADDITIONAL COMMENTS

CLASSIFICATION AND MORPHOLOGY
AND LOCOMOTION

Common name_____   Common name_____

Infraorder_____   Infraorder_____

Superfamily_____   Superfamily_____

Family_____   Family_____

Subfamily_____   Subfamily_____

Genus_____   Genus_____

Species_____   Species_____

Distribution_____   Distribution_____

Tail?_____   Tail?_____

Prehensile tail?_____   Prehensile tail?_____

Nails on all digits?_____   Nails on all digits?_____

Relative length of forelimbs to   Relative length of forelimbs to
   hindlimbs_____   hindlimbs_____

Habitual mode of locomotion   Habitual mode of locomotion
_____   _____

Sexual dimorphism in body size_____   Sexual dimorphism in body size_____

ADDITIONAL COMMENTS

PRIMATE OBSERVATION

Name_____ Date_____ Beginning Time _____

<u>Scan Sampling for Focal Animal</u>

Species:_____Common Name:_____

Composition of group: Number of Adult Males_____ Adult Females_____

Immature individuals_____ Group Size _____

Brief Description of Weather:

Description of Focal Animal:

Age-Grade (Adult, Juvenile, Infant):

Sex:

OBSERVATIONS:

PRIMATE OBSERVATION

Name_____   Date_____ Beginning Time _____

Scan Sampling for Focal Animal

Species:_____Common Name:_____

Composition of group: Number of Adult Males_____ Adult Females_____

                              Immature individuals_____ Group Size _____

Brief Description of Weather:

Description of Focal Animal:

Age-Grade (Adult, Juvenile, Infant):

Sex:

OBSERVATIONS:

CHECKLIST OF PRIMATE BEHAVIORS
Focal Animal

Number of Occurrences in 30 sec. or 1 minute

	1	2	3	4	5	6	7	8	9	10	11	12	13	14	15	16	17	18	19	20
Walking																				
Sitting																				
Prone																				
Standing																				
Eating																				
Scratching																				
Vocalizing																				
Sleeping																				
Autogrooming																				
Grooming/Groomed																				
Displaying																				
Threat/Threatened																				
Chase/Chased																				
Attack/Attacked																				
Playing																				
Courtship/Courted																				
Mount/Mounted																				
Present																				
Displace/Displaced																				
Other (explain)																				
Other (explain)																				
Other (explain)																				

Chapter 9

Paleocene-Eocene Primate Evolution

(Prosimii & possible appearance of Anthropoidea)

INTRODUCTION

While the near 30 million year duration of the Paleocene and Eocene epochs together make up just under half of the Cenozoic Era, we will spend little time in the laboratory investigating the fossil primates of these epochs.

The era preceding the Paleocene, the Mesozoic Era, occurred between 230 and 65 millions of years ago (m.y.a.). It is popularly known as the Age of Reptiles, or the the Age of Dinosaurs because these sometimes huge animals were the dominant form of land fauna during this period. Nevertheless, less than one-third of the way into the era (at roughly 200 m.y.a.), the first mammals appeared on the fossil record. Although these mammals continued to evolve and diversify through the remainder of this era, they remained quite small in size and numbers relative to the dinosaurs and other vertebrates. This situation changed dramatically with the extinction, at the end of the Meso-zoic, of not only the dinosaurs, but up to 60% of all terrestrial and marine animals. Among the animals to survive this catastrophe were small insect-eating mammals. From these insectivores many orders of the mammals (including primates) radiated and flourished in econiches left vacant by the mass extinc-tions, giving rise to the Age of Mammals, as the Cenozoic Era is sometimes known.

THE PALEOCENE – *Appearance of Prosimii*

The primates of the first epoch of the Cenozoic, the Paleocene Epoch (65 to 54 m.y.a.), have been found only in North America and Europe. They are odd, little-understood animals which do not greatly resemble primates of succeeding epochs. In fact, the primates of the Paleocene are classified as primates only because of the primate-like morphology of their molar teeth and because of the construction of the bony capsule that encloses the middle ear. These are both derived characters which are unlike those of their insectivore ancestors.

Plesiadapis (Figure 9.1) is one of the most complete Paleocene primate skeletons known. Specimens of this genus, found in France and Colorado, are virtually identical. Note the almost equal lengths of the hind- and fore-limbs; the claws on all of the digits; the absence of a post-orbital bar; the lateral orientation of the eye orbits; the small brain case; the large, heavy muzzle; the large incisors; and the gap between the large anterior and cheek teeth. These are not characteristics found in either living primates or a vast majority of fossil primates of succeeding epochs. Plesiadapis, in fact, and some other genera of Paleocene primates, are more rodent- than primate-like (with the exception of the morphology of the molars and the inner ear) and possibly occupied rodent-like niches, as true rodents did not evolve until the Eocene Epoch.

Palaechthon (Figure 9.2) was an insect-eating Paleocene primate. It probably closely resembles the primitive primates, as it is less specialized than the rodent-like Plesiadapis. An animal such as Palaechthon, therefore, would have been unspecialized enough to give

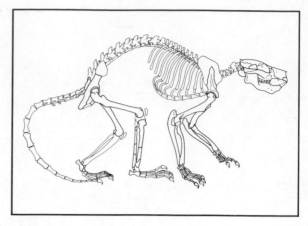

Figure 9.1 Plesiadapis
(courtesy of I. Tattersall)

Figure 9.2 Palaechthon
(courtesy of A. A. Knopf, Inc.)

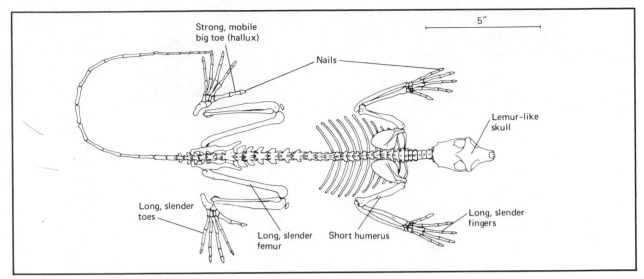

Figure 9.3 <u>Notharctus</u> (courtesy of A. A. Knopf, Inc.)

rise both to primates like <u>Plesia-</u><u>dapis</u> and more advanced primates of the Eocene epoch.

THE EOCENE

← Prosimians, now Anthropoidea

Primates of the succeeding epoch, the Eocene (54 - 36 m.y.a.), are undoubtedly primates, and are found in North America, Europe and Asia. They are, with the possible excep-tion of some primates found in Burma at the very end of the epoch (near 40 m.y.a.) (Ciochon et al. 1985), all of the prosimian grade of evolution.

More advanced primates appear in the early Eocene fossil record in North America and Europe (and a bit later in Asia). These are undoubt-edly primates, as they closely resemble some of the living prosim-ians, and had significantly larger brains than other animals of the same time period. While the pri-mate fauna of the early Eocene of North America and Europe were still very similar, they began to appear more distinctive as an ocean gap (the North Atlantic Ocean) began to open up as the plates on which the continents ride drifted apart.

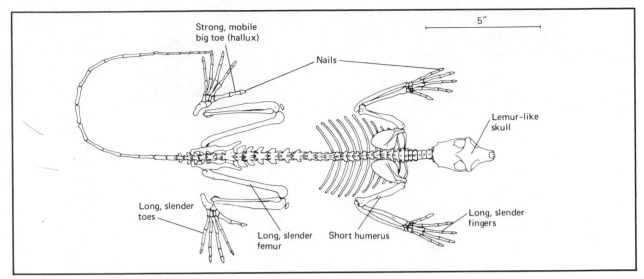

Figure 9.4 <u>Adapis</u>
(courtesy of A. A. Knopf, Inc.)

later
∨ Eocene → the continents of NORTH AMERICA and EUROPE began to drift apart (north Atlantic Ocean gap)

Nevertheless, prosimians continued to flourish on North America, Europe and Asia throughout the Eocene. _Notharctus_ and _Adapis_ are the two Eocene primates which will be studied here.

Exercises

1. Study the Paleocene (Figures 9.1 and 9.2) and the Eocene primates (Figures 9.3 and 9.4). Which group relied more on their sense of sight in locating food and avoiding danger? State the rationale behind your answer.

2. Was the sense of smell more developed in Paleocene or Eocene primates? State the rationale behind your answer.

3. Study the skull and skeleton of <u>Northarctus</u> (Figure 9.3) and the skull of
    <u>Adapis</u> (Figure 9.4). Compare these Eocene primates with those of the
    Paleocene and with modern prosimians. Make a list of the characteristics
    in which Eocene primates more closely resemble modern prosimians than
    Paleocene prosimians.

    What does this list tell you of the Eocene primates?

4. Do you believe the Eocene primates were arboreal or terrestrial? Why?

5. Some of the Eocene prosimians were believed to be nocturnal and others
    diurnal. How can one determine whether a fossil animal was nocturnal or
    diurnal? Study the eye-orbits of a modern nocturnal bushbaby (Figure 7.2),
    then observe the eye-orbits of a monkey or other diurnal mammal in your
    laboratory (while making compensations for differences in body size).

SUBORDER: Prosimii   Anthropoidea

Hominoidea

Chapter 10

Oligocene Primate Evolution

35 mya — Anthropoidea & appearance of Hominoidea

~53 mya

As the end of the Eocene epoch approached, the earth's climate was becoming cooler. Subtropical forests of North America and Europe were replaced by grasslands and woodlands suited for a more seasonal climate. The prosimians which had thrived on these continents during Paleocene-Eocene times began to disappear. *∴ AFRICAN CONTINENT*

We pick up the course of Old World primate evolution during the succeeding Oligocene Epoch (36 - 23 m.y.a.) on the African continent where so much of the primate evolution has occurred (including the early stage of our genus, Homo). Unfortunately, only one primate fossil site is known, the Fayum depression of Egypt in the northeast corner of the continent (Figure 10.1). Fossil primates of this age have not yet been found in the rainforest area of central Africa near the equator where primate evolution of later epochs (Miocene to present) was centered and where it may have been centered in the Oligocene.

THE FAYUM *(Egypt - Northern corner of Africa)*

The Fayum today has a desert climate, but during the Oligocene this same area was much wetter with mixed habitats of fresh water swamps bordered by grass- lands and woodlands in which the primates lived (Olson and Rasmussen 1986).

Some of the Fayum fossil primates are the first well-known anthropoids or higher primates (as mentioned above, some primate jaws of the late Eocene in

Burma may be anthropoids, but the remains of these fossil primates are still quite fragmentary). The Fayum primates have been known since the first decade of this century but most of the specimens we have today have been collected since the 1960's. At various times, several Fayum primate species have been identified by different researchers as the very earliest hominid, the earliest pongid (great ape), the earliest hylobatid (lesser ape), the earliest Old World monkey, the common ancestor of all hominoids, or common ancestor of all catarrhines (Old World monkeys, apes and humans). Most of these relation-ships were advanced when the Fayum species were known from only a few speci-mens and most of the specimens were parts of jaws and teeth only. However, since the 1960's fossil-hunting expeditions of Elwyn Simons and his colleagues have greatly increased the number of Fayum primate specimens and have, there-fore, greatly enhanced our view of primate evolution during the Oligocene.

While some of the Fayum primates are still seen as having reached the status of "higher" primates, they are seen as very primitive higher primates. One of the few skulls of a Fayum primate, Aegyptopithecus zeuxis (Figure 10.3), in fact, has some resemblances to known Eocene prosimian skulls. This is to be expected of a primitive anthropoid. The relationship of the Fayum primates to primates of succeeding epochs is not clear-cut; direct ancestral-descendant relationships between Oligocene primates and the primates of the succeeding Miocene epoch, for instance, are difficult to determine from the presently available data (see Fleagle and Kay 1983, for a recent review). In fact, the classification of the Oligocene primates is a bit up in the air at present (Ciochon 1983). In view of these classification difficulties, the Fayum pri-mates are presented in two groups as follows:

Family   Parapithecidae
   Genera   Parapithecus
                   Apidium

                The "Propliopiths"
   Genera   Propliopithecus - 3 species
                   Aegyptopithecus - 1 species
                   Oligopithecus (?)

Parapithecus was a small (mouse-lemur sized) primate. It has sometimes been considered a possible Old World monkey ancestor because of certain features of its teeth (e.g., incipient bilophodont molars). However, it exhibits a number of very primitive cranial and postcranial features which suggest that it could not have figured in the ancestry of Old World monkeys and apes (Fleagle and Kay 1983).

The Parapithecidae had 3 premolars in each quadrant like the New World mon-keys. In fact, some believe that some of these primates may have made their way from Africa across the Atlantic Ocean (which was much narrower in the Oligocene), and may have given rise to the New World primates (see Ciochon and Chiarelli 1980).

The Propliopiths (Figures 10.2 and 10.3) are approximately 30 to 35 m.y.a., and are much more likely to be related to the Miocene hominoids in which we will be interested, and therefore will be stressed here. These animals have the same dental formula as living Old World higher primates (2 premolars in each quadrant). Notice also the broad patterns of the dention of the Propliopiths: the shape of the dental arcade; the size of the canines; and the morphology of the cheek teeth, and refer back to the discussion of the dental characteristics of living primates. It is easy to understand why these primates have often been called "dental apes." Because of the broad similarities of the dentition of the Propliopiths and later apes, they have often been classified in the same superfamily as living apes, the Hominoidea (Fleagle and Kay 1983). In fact, some have suggested that the Fayum Propliopiths may represent something from which both the Old World monkeys and the apes could be derived. Certainly the Propliopiths seem unspecialized and primitive enough to serve as possible ancestors for both groups of Old World higher primates (Fleagle and Kay 1983). In any case, something like Propliopithecus or Aegyptopithecus could have been the ancestor of the early Miocene hominoids, the "Dryopiths". The Dryopiths, as we shall see, probably did figure in the ancestry of living great apes and ourselves.

Before we get carried away pointing out the ape-like characteristics of the Propliopiths, let us observe some of the characteristics which suggest that they are also very primitive anthropoids. We might begin by asking the question, what are the characteristics necessary to be ranked as an anthropoid? To answer this question, look at the cranium of Aegyptopithecus and compare it to that of the Eocene prosimian, Adapis, (Figure 9.4). It can be seen that Aegyptopithecus had a rather long, large snout like some of the Eocene prosimians and unlike the majority of anthropoids of later epochs. The snout of Aegyptopithecus is seen as a primitive trait relative to later higher primates which possessed much reduced snouts. Now study the eye orbits of Aegyptopithecus. You can see that the eye orbits are almost completely enclosed with bone. This is considered an anthropoid, or higher primate characteristic, as all anthropoids and only one living prosimian, the tarsier, possesses this trait (see Figure 10.4).

Aegyptopithecus possesses another anthropoid characteristic: a fused mandibular symphysis. The symphysis is the area where the two halves of the mandible meet (at the midline between the two medial incisors). The symphyseal region of living prosimians is not fused and comes apart after death.

Because of these higher primate traits, Aegyptopithecus and Propliopithecus are considered to

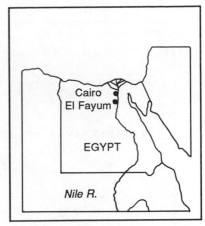

Figure 10.1 Fayum, Egypt (AFRICAN CONTINENT)

Kenyapithecus & Ramapithecus why did early workers think they were hominids? Why no monkey? or apes?

129

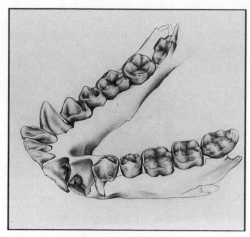

Figure 10.2 Mandible
of Propliopithecus
(courtesy of R. Kay)

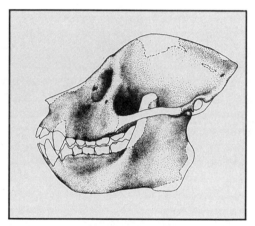

Figure 10.3 Skull of
Aegyptopithecus
(courtesy of R. Kay)

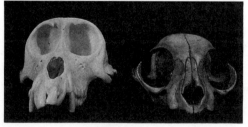

Figure 10.4 Enclosed eye
orbits of monkey, (left),
not enclosed in cat (right)

have reached the anthropoid grade that is to be at the monkey- and ape-like level of evolution. However, terms such as "monkey-" or "ape-like", when applied to Oligocene primates, is very misleading. These Propliopiths were primitive relative to living monkeys and apes.

Studies of the postcranial remains of the Fayum Propliopiths reinforces the view gained from the study of their skulls that they were quite primitive.

Unfortunately, nothing close to a complete skeleton of a Propliopith has yet been uncovered, but several limb bones believed to be of the Propliopiths have been found at Fayum. Comparisons of these fossil limb bones with those of living primates shows that they were more primitive than any of the groups of higher primates (Fleagle and Kay 1983, Fleagle and Simons 1978). The Propliopiths postcranially may have been somewhat like the large New World monkeys, (e.g. the howler monkey), and they were probably slow-moving arboreal quadrupeds.

1. What do the cranial characteristics of <u>Aegyptopithecus</u> suggest about the relative importance of the senses of smell and sight?

2. <u>Aegyptopithecus</u> possesses a small sagittal crest. What does this suggest about the brain size of this animal?

3. What value would you expect for the condylar index in <u>Aegyptopithecus</u>?

4. Compare the Aegyptopithecus eye orbits (in size, relative enclosure and and position) with those of living prosimians, monkeys and apes, and humans.

Proconsul - early Miocene Hominid
- elbow & shoulder joints like a chimpazees
- wrist like a monkey
- lumbar vertebrae like a gibbon

Dryopithecus major - ancestor of Gorilla
- 22-17 mya
- not all Dryopithecines have U-shaped dentition (D. major does!)

Sivapithecus: - Pakistan 8 mya
- Facial remains ⇒ concave profile and projecting incisors (like Pongo?)

Gigantopithecus - late Miocene to the early Pleistocene
- has Y5 cusps (seen on one specimen)
- existed for 10 mys → why is it said that it was prob. a vegetarian?

Chapter 11

Miocene Hominid Evolution

[handwritten annotations:]
25 mya   Prosimii   Anthropoidea
-5 mya   \ Hominoidea
                                              / |
                                        Pongidae   hominids
                               (probable appearance)

INTRODUCTION

Most evidence points to the Miocene (23 - 5.5 m.y.a.) as the epoch during which the pongid and hominid lineages diverged. It is an epoch, therefore, of primary interest and importance to paleoanthropologists. The questions concerning Miocene hominoid evolution can be summarized as follows:

1. What is the branching order of living and fossil primates?
2. What are the dates of the branching points that led to the living and fossil hominoids? Which of the living apes was the last to share a common ancestor with humans?
3. What did the last common ancestor of humans and apes look like? How did it move? What did it eat? In what type of habitat did it live? On what continent or continents of the Old World did it evolve?

Unfortunately, absolute answers are known for <u>none</u> of these intriguing questions, due primarily to the lack of hominoid fossil data during certain crucial periods at different locations, and because almost no fossil apes are known in Africa that are more recent than 13 million years old. Analysis and interpretation of the data available vary widely, so no consensus exists today among paleoanthropologists as to the course of Miocene hominoid evolution. The physical aspects of our own evolution are fairly well understood from about 4 million years ago - the date of appearance of a well-known hominid genus, <u>Australopithecus</u>.

We will examine some of the data available today, as well as some of the suggested interpretations of such data offered by paleoanthropologists. The student is encouraged to develop his/her own solution to this puzzle which can be modified as new fossils are discovered and other data become available.

Though we are very interested in our own evolution, we should remember that evolutionary models of man must also include the apes, so an understanding of the branching order of the hominoids is necessary before intelligent models of hominoid evolution can be made. Since it will be some time before we have the fossils to elucidate this question, we look to the molecular-biochemical data to help us.

THE BIOMOLECULAR DATA

One approach used to attempt to determine the branching order to the hominoids is to compare the genomes (DNA) and the biochemistry (including the proteins) of the living hominoids.

Theoretically, the best way to compare the nuclear DNA (DNA in the chromosomes of all nuclei) is to compare each base pair in each chromosome of the genera being compared. This would be difficult, as there are up to three billion base pairs in the genomes of hominoids! Therefore, a number of indirect methods have been used by molecular anthropologists to compare genomes, including the comparison of the relative similarity of individual proteins among primates and especially among hominoids. These tests indicate a difference of only 1 or 2 percent between the nuclear DNA of humans and chimpanzees; slightly more between humans and the gorillas, and about twice that between humans and orang-utans. This similarity was surprising because the behavioral, ecological and morphological differences between humans and our non-speaking quadrupedal, forest-living relatives might indicate a larger difference. This suggests that only a small amount of the genome is responsible for the differences observed between humans and apes (King and Wilson 1975).

–Regulatory genes direct structural genes to regulate development of organism

"Regulatory genes" have been hypothesized as being responsible for the differences observed in morphology and behavior between apes and humans (Raff and Kaufman 1983). These genes, making up only a small part of the genome, would regulate the development of organisms using "structural genes" which make up most of the genome. If this is found to be true, it would be interesting to research the similarity of the regulatory genes of extant hominoids to see if they are as similar to each other as are the structural genes.

Many different biomolecular techniques have yielded several different branching sequences in the hominoid line (Templeton 1983; see Figure 11.1). All of the phylogenies, however, are in agreement in a few areas. All have shown conclusively that the monkeys are more distantly related to humans than are the hominoids. Among the hominoids, gibbons and siamangs (Hylobates sps.) are more distantly related to Homo than are the great apes. Further, most analyses (but not all) of the biomolecular data show the African apes to be more closely related to man than is the lone remaining Asian great ape, Pongo. This view of the branching sequence of the living hominoids is not new: ever since the time of Darwin and Thomas Huxley, most comparative morphological studies have supported the view that the African apes are more closely related to humans than are any other primates. For years, however, biomolecular techniques were unable to separate the Gorilla, Pan, and Homo triad.

134

DNA Hybridization

DNA-DNA hybridization is a recent technique which may have taken us a long way toward solving the branching question. As we have disovered, the double helix of nuclear DNA in organisms consists of two strands of nucleotides bound together at the organic bases. At very high temperatures (approximately 100 degrees Celsius), however, the double strands can be separated into single strands. In this technique, single strands of DNA of one species are matched with single strands of another species. The greater the base-pair similarities between the strands of DNA, the greater the degree of re-bonding between them. The two bonded strands from different species are then reheated, but because of the incomplete bonding, will separate at lower temperatures than that needed to separate the original double helix. When the nuclear DNA of several species is compared in this way, the difference in temperatures needed to separate the strands is used to calculate relative genetic similarities and possible phylogenetic relationships of the species being compared.

The DNA-DNA hybridization technique has recently been applied to primates (Sibley and Ahlquist 1984). The results of this technique strongly support phylogeny "a" of Figure 11.1; that is, the chimpanzee is more closely related to humans than is the gorilla.

This technique would seem to be superior to previous biomolecular techniques because it uses a much greater portion of the genome in making comparisons between species. Not everyone is convinced, however, that this technique is strong enough to delineate the obviously very small genetic differences between chimps, gorillas and humans. In addition, it is clear that this technique measures the interspecific differences in the DNA chain, but we don't know how closely those differences correspond to the behavioral and morphological differences, nor do they tell us how evolution is proceeding. For instance, as stated before, most analyses indicate that the nuclear DNA of _Pongo_ differs from that of humans by 2 to 4 percent. Which animal, therefore, has retained more ancestral DNA; the humans or the orang-utan? Which has evolved at a faster rate and therefore shows more change in the nuclear DNA?

As this brief review has illustrated, we still do not have a branching order agreed upon by all of the molecular-biochemical anthropologists. Nonetheless, most favor one of the first four phylogenies of Figure 11.1, in which the chimpanzee (phylogeny "a") or the gorilla (phylogeny "b"), or both (phylogenies "c" and "d") were the last to share a common ancestor with humans. The fossil evidence supports this notion since the first known hominids (_Australopithecus_) are found in Africa. As we have seen, the DNA-DNA hybridization technique strongly supports phylogeny "a". A very small minority of anthropologists favor phylogenies "e" and "f", in which the orang-utan is more closely related to humans (Schwartz 1984).

THE "MOLECULAR CLOCK"

Since the late 1960s a few biomolecular biologists and anthropologists have proposed that not only can the branching sequences be derived from the biochemical-molecular data, but that the _dates_ of those sequences can be provided as well. The first such clocks (using an immunological technique for estimating genetic distance between living hominoids) indicated that all hominoid evolution occurred in the last 10 million years (Sarich and Wilson 1967;

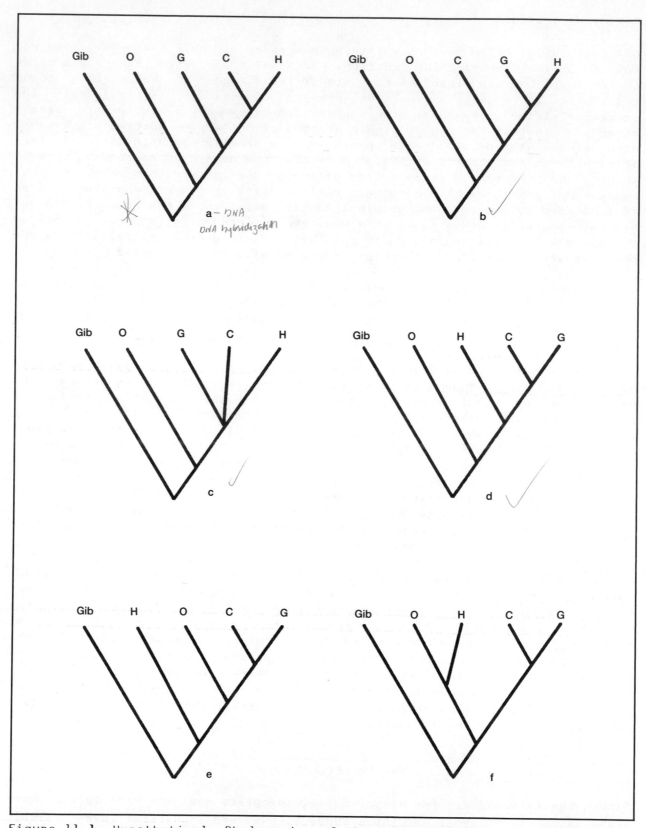

Figure 11.1 Hypothetical Phylogenies of the Hominoidea, Based on Various
Biochemical and Molecular Data
Key: Gib = Gibbon and Siamang, O = Orang-utan,
G = Gorilla, C = Chimpanzee, H = Humans

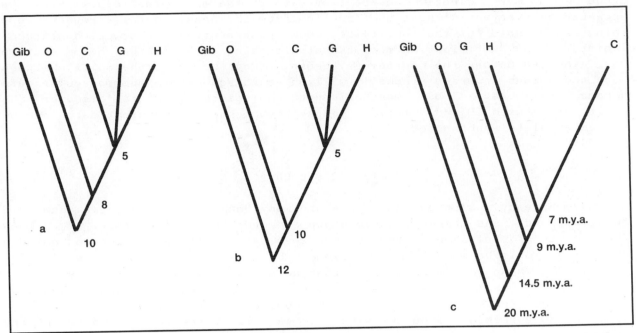

Figure 11.2 Molecular Clock Phylogenies
   (a) After Sarich and Wilson, 1967; (b) After Cronin, 1983; (c) After Sibley
and Ahlquist, 1984
             Key: Gib = Gibbon and Siamang, O = Orang-utan,
                   G = Gorilla, C = Chimpanzee, H = Humans

Figure 11.2).   This clock has since been modified and others proposed (Cronin
1983, Gingerich 1984, Sibley and Ahlquist 1984).

In all of these techniques a calibration date is derived from at least one
branching date from the hominoid fossil data, and then the other branching
dates of the living hominids are calculated using the genetic distances calculated from the biomolecular data.   The earliest version of the clock gained
little support from paleoanthropologists because the fossil data strongly suggested that all of hominoid evolution could not have occurred in only the last
10 million years.   In fact, recent fossil discoveries have suggested that the
lineage which led to the orang-utan branched off from the lineages leading to
African apes and humans at between 13 and 16 million years ago (Pilbeam 1984,
see below).

Moreover, many criticisms of the molecular clock have been made by researchers
who work primarily with the biochemical-molecular data (e.g. Goodman et al.
1983).   Many of these researchers doubt that an accurate clock can be derived
strictly from the molecular data.   Some of the biomolecular data suggest that
our lineage has evolved at a rate which is 2 to 3 times slower than the com-
bined gorilla-chimp lineage (Templeton 1983, 1985).   This agrees with the
current paradigm debate of gradualism versus punctuated equilibrium which
suggests that different lineages evolved at different rates.   Some advocates
of the molecular clocks, on the other hand, argue that the biomolecular data
alone indicates that all hominoid lineages evolved at uniform rates (Cronin
1983, Sibley and Ahlquist 1984).

Much more information concerning the mode of evolution, possible variation in
the rates of evolution, and relationships to the molecular data must be under-

stood much more clearly before that data of the molecular clock will be accepted by everyone without confirmation from the fossil data. However, one thing can be said for the "molecular clock" controversy: most paleoanthropologists are now anticipating more recent branching dates of the hominoids than was expected before the controversy began. Most believed the split between apes and humans occurred around 15 million years ago before the molecular data became available. Today most paleoanthropologists expect to discover the split at between 10 and 5 million years (though the more ancient date cannot yet be absolutely abandoned).

THE FOSSIL DATA

We have already indicated that there are many "gaps" in the Miocene hominoid fossil record, and the most serious gap concerns the African apes. If we knew the course of evolution of the chimpanzees and gorillas, Miocene hominoid evolution would be much less mysterious, but, as mentioned, there are few fossil apes known in Africa younger than about 13 m.y.a. Also, while several small Miocene fossil primates have been proposed as possible gibbon ancestors, the evidence for hylobatid evolution is quite scanty at present and there is little agreement among the experts. We will therefore not consider the ancestory of the gibbons and siamangs further, nor will we address the evolution of the Miocene fossil monkeys and apes which do not bear on the ancestry of extant great apes and humans.

Because it is not yet clear how the Miocene apes are related to each other and to living apes, their classification is in a state of confusion. As stated, biological classification should reflect, as much as is understood, the phylogeny of the animals, and this pertains as well to fossil evolution. Although evolutionary relationships are not clearly understood at present, we will divide the Miocene fossil apes and the ancestors to humans into two groups: "Dryopiths" and "Ramapiths". The genera included in these two groups, their location and known ages are listed.

GROUP	GENERA	LOCATION AND AGES
Dryopiths	Proconsul	Africa 23 m.y.a. - 13 m.y.a.
	Dryopithecus	Europe 16 m.y.a. - 12 m.y.a.
Ramapiths	Ramapithecus	Europe and Asia 14 m.y.a. - 7 m.y.a.
	Kenyapithecus	Africa 14 m.y.a.
	Sivapithecus	Africa, Europe and Asia 17 m.y.a. - 7 m.y.a.
	Ouranopithecus	S. E. Europe 10 m.y.a.
	Gigantopithecus	India and China 8 m.y.a. - 1 m.y.a.

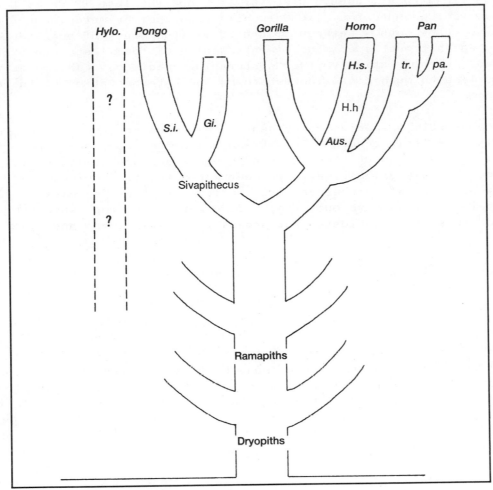

Figure 11.3 Phylogenetic Scheme Based on Fossil Data
Key: <u>Hylo.</u> = Gibbon and Siamang, <u>Pongo</u> = Orang-utan,
<u>H.s.</u> = <u>Homo</u> <u>sapiens</u>, <u>H.h.</u> = <u>Homo</u> <u>habilis</u>,
<u>Aus.</u> = <u>Australopithecus</u>, <u>tr.</u> = <u>Pan</u> <u>troglodytes</u>
<u>pa.</u> = <u>Pan</u> <u>paniscus</u>, <u>S.i.</u> = <u>S. indicus</u>,
<u>Gi.</u> = <u>Gigantopithecus</u>

THE DRYOPITHS

The Dryopiths include the very first fossil ape that was described in scientific literature; a mandible of <u>Dryopithecus fontani</u> was found near Saint Gaudens in southern France and described in 1856 (Lartet 1856). We now know that European species of <u>Dryopithecus</u> appeared later than <u>Proconsul</u> and are most likely derived from <u>Proconsul</u> species of the early Miocene of East Africa. It would appear, in fact, that the first radiation of the Dryopiths took place at the very end of the Oligocene or at the beginning of the Miocene at around 23 m.y.a. It would also appear that one or more of the <u>Proconsul</u> species figured in the evolution of all of the living larger hominoids, including ourselves, so we now concentrate on <u>Proconsul</u>.

African Dryopiths

The early Miocene of East Africa is an exception to the generally fossil-poor record of African fossil apes. Discoveries since the late 1930s in Uganda and Kenya have yielded more than 1,000 fossils of higher primates, most of which are believed to be apes, between 13 and 23 million years of age. However, it must be noted that most specimens of this wealth of fossil apes are teeth and jaw fragments with relatively fewer postcranial specimens. This, as we shall see, can lead to much confusion regarding the interpretation of these fossil apes.

There are currently 5 species described in the genus Proconsul. The smallest two species of this genus (P. [Rangwapithecus] gordoni and P. [R.] vancouveringi) are about the size of gibbons and are believed to be too specialized to have given rise to younger known fossil hominoids and living apes. Therefore, we will consider here the largest three species of Proconsul (listed below) which have more generalized morphology and which have been considered possible candidates for ancestry of later large apes (see Figure 11.3).

        Proconsul africanus   arboreal monkey-sized (20-30 lbs.)
        P. nyanzae   chimpanzee-sized
        P. major   female gorilla-sized

Paleoanthropologists in the recent past have postulated direct ancestral-descendant relationships between Proconsul and the living African apes (Proconsul africanus to Pan, for example). While these direct relationships receive little support today, most paleoanthropologists would agree that these early Miocene primates, at least dentally, are candidates for the ancestry of African apes and other fossil hominoids of the middle to late Miocene.

Though most of the dental characteristics of Proconsul are generalized enough to be ancestral to modern apes, one dental feature in this Miocene form is considered primitive.   Extant apes generally have no cingula (small "shelves" on the lingual side of the upper molars and cheek sides of the lower molars) as shown in an Oligocene primate in Figure 10.2.

Teeth alone, however, do not make an ape.   The paleoenvironmental and post-cranial data of Proconsul are also important.

The paleoenvironmental data (primarily fossil plants and animals) suggest that the areas of Uganda and Kenya where Proconsul specimens are found were to a large extent rainforest with some dry forest to woodland settings (Pickford 1983). Most of the Proconsul species were likely forest-living and arboreal, though some of the larger species like P. major and P. nyanzae may have been at least partially terrestrial.

The postcranial remains of Proconsul, as mentioned above, are very rare in-deed. Most of what we know of the postcranial skeleton of Proconsul comes from one specimen, the P. africanus specimen pictured in Figure 11.4. Parts of the skull, the jaws and teeth, and most of the left forearm of this speci-men were found in 1948, and recently, additional pieces of the same specimen were discovered in museum and laboratory collections in Kenya. The studies of the forelimb resulted in conflicting interpretations of the locomotor habits and phylogenetic position of P. africanus. This specimen has been described as ape-like to monkey-like, a brachiator, an incipient knuckle-walker or

quadrupedal monkey by different
investigators. Among other things,
these studies demonstrate that
paleontologists and paleoanthropologists have traditionally exag-
gerated the knowledge which can be
gained from the study of a few
parts of a fossil skeleton. Complete or nearly complete skeletons
are needed.

We may soon have a much sharper
picture of Proconsul as new finds
are described, but a recent preliminary study of the nearly complete P. africanus specimen indicates that it was postcranially a
primitive, unspecialized hominoid
(Walker and Pickford 1983). It
was robust and powerful for such a
small (25 lb.) primate and was
probably a slow-moving arboreal
quadruped capable of various locomotor and feeding postures. It had
none of the postcranial speciali-
zations of extant apes (e.g. longer forelimbs relative to hindlimbs associated with brachiation
or knuckle-walking.

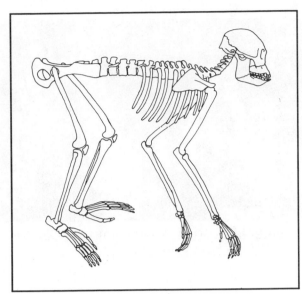

Figure 11.4 Proconsul africanus
(courtesy of A. Walker)

European Dryopiths

The appearance of Dryopithecus in
Europe is associated with a major
geological event: the formation of
a land connection between Africa
and Eurasia at about 17 to 16
million years ago. This bridge
allowed widespread migration between the two huge landmasses that
had not been possible before.
Hence, at least one population of
Proconsul or Proconsul-like apes
moved to the woodlands of Europe
and eventually became genetically
isolated from parent populations
in Africa. Europe at this time had
a seasonal climate, but the win-
ters were much milder and the
woodlands and forests were more
widespread than today. The postcranial remains of the European
Dryopithecus species are even more
scarce than Proconsul postcranial
remains.

Figure 11.5 Chimpanzee (left)
Sivapithecus indicus (center)
Orang-utan (right)
(courtesy of D. Pilbeam)

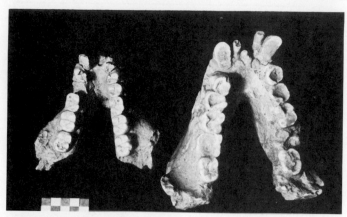

Figure 11.6 G. bilaspurensis (right)
G. blacki (right)

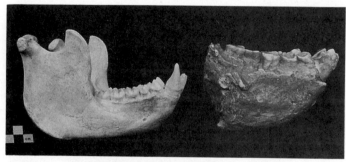

Figure 11.7 Gorilla (left)
G. blacki (right)

Ramapith fossils range in size from that of a medium-sized monkey to larger than the largest living primate. They were first discovered in the early part of this century in the Siwalik Hills of the Indian subcontinent (Himalayan foothills). Most of these early finds were believed to be apes and were placed in the genus Sivapithecus (after the Hindu God, Shiva; pronounced "Shivapithicus"). In the early 1930s, Edward Lewis found a fragment of a maxilla in the Siwalik Hills and described it as a possible hominid, Ramapithecus. Lewis's claims were largely ignored until the 1960s when Elwyn Simons, and later, David Pilbeam, described the possible affinities of Ramapithecus and the first hominids, the Australopithecines (Simons and Pilbeam 1965).

Other fossil teeth and jaws were found in India, Pakistan and Africa, and were placed in the same genus. A specimen of Ramapithecus from Ft. Ternan, Kenya, is now called Kenyapithecus, (the original name given by Louis Leakey, its discoverer), is dated at 13 - 14 m.y.a. Since Ramapithecus existed more recently than Proconsul, Ramapithecus (and probably Sivapithecus) possibly evolved from one or more of the early Miocene Proconsul species of East Africa and migrated to Euraisa after 16 m.y.

13-14 mya

Ramapithecus exhibits many features in the jaws and teeth which are also found in the Pliocene fossils of Australopithecus. Ramapithecus

142

was, therefore, on the basis of these similarities, considered to be a hominid and to be ancestral to Australopithecus. Since the Ramapithecus (Kenyapithecus) specimen at Ft. Ternan is dated at around 14 m.y. and the specimens of Eurasia slightly younger, a date of about 15 m.y. was proposed for the split of the hominid lineage from those of the apes (Proconsul).

Much has occurred, however, which has modified this view of hominoid evolution. As was discussed above, the biomolecular data which began to appear in the late 1960s indicated a much more recent date for the hominid - ape split. In addition, further comparisons of Ramapithecus and Sivapithecus have shown them to be much more similar to each other than was formerly recognized (Pilbeam 1984). In fact some now feel that the two groups of fossil apes should be classified in the same genus (Greenfield 1979, Kay and Simons 1983).

Sivapithecus indicus

David Pilbeam and others have identified several new Ramapith specimens from the Siwalik Hills in Pakistan. These fossils strongly indicate that Sivapithecus may be close to the ancestry of the orang-utan (Andrews 1983, Pilbeam 1984;). In particular, one specimen which includes a partial face of a rather large ape assigned to the species Sivapithecus indicus shows many orang-utan-like features (Figure 11.5). These features are especially remarkable because this fossil (specimen GSP 15000)is dated at 8 m.y.a. These similarities do not necessarily imply a direct ancestral-descendant relationship of Sivapithecus indicus to Pongo, but it does strongly suggest that some of the Asian Ramapiths figured in the ancestry of the living orang-utans.

Though the face of this Sivapithecus indicus specimen shows detailed affinities to extant Pongo, the mandible is only broadly similar (Ward and Pilbeam 1983). This phenomenon may be explained by the concept of **mosaic evolution**. This hypothesis states that different parts of an organism might evolve at different rates at different times. In another example, we have seen that even though Proconsul had teeth and jaws that are similar to those of living apes (while not disregarding the differences), from the neck down these primitive hominoids were not particularly similar to living apes.

Unfortunately, even less is known of the postcrania of the Ramapiths than is known of the Dryopiths. Only isolated limb bone fragments have been discovered, though most studies agree that by at least 15 to 10 million years ago, Ramapith forelimbs had begun to show anatomical patterns characteristic of living great apes and humans. The Ramapiths seem to have possessed generalized ape bodies underlying generalized locomotor and postural capabilities (Rose 1983).

In what type of habitats did the Ramapiths live? All of the sites, whether in Africa or southern Eurasia, are associated with mixed habitats of seasonal woodlands interspersed with open grasslands. They have not been associated with rainforest habitats, as were many of the early Miocene Dryopiths. Almost nothing can be said about Ramapith locomotion except that they were capable of generalized ape movements. But presumably, the smaller ones were more arboreal while the larger ones must have exhibited a terrestrial component in their locomotor behavior.

Gigantopithecus

Gigantopithecus bilaspurensis (Figure 11.6) was discovered in the Siwalik Hills of India and is believed to be derived from a large Sivapithecus. While it is thought to be about 8 million years old, G. blacki specimens discovered in China are much younger, probably less than 1 million years old.

One cannot judge the size of a fossil animal from the size of the mandible alone, but weight estimates from this Gigantopithecus specimen begin at about 600 lbs, and it may well have weighed more than 800 lbs! Today we have only a few fossil limb fragments that may be those of Gigantopithecus, so we have almost no knowledge of how they may have moved through the mixed habitats of South Asia of that time period, but they are so large that they must have been entirely terrestrial.

Eurasian Ramapiths

The earliest Eurasian Ramapiths are at least 13 million years old (Raza et al. 1983). It seems clear that some of the Ramapiths moved from Africa to the Eurasian continent after the African and Eurasian plates collided, as discussed above. Since the Asian Ramapiths (more specifically Sivapithecus) are now believed to figure in the ancestry of the living orang-utan, a date of between 13 and 16 million years ago has been suggested for the split between the lineages of Pongo and those that led to the African great apes and humans (Pilbeam 1984).

SUMMARY

1. Anatomical comparisons of living hominoids and the biomolecular data suggest it is most probable that the branching order of the hominoids has the small ape (hylobatid) ancestor branching off first, then that of the orang-utan, then those leading to the hominids and the African apes (phylogenies "a" through "d", Figure 11.1).

2. The possibility that the lineage leading to the hominids' last shared ancestry with that leading to the orang-utan (phylogenies "e" and "f" in Figure 11.1.) is much less probable than the above scenario.

3. The biomolecular and fossil data available suggest it is probable that the last human-ape ancestor lived sometime between 10 and 5 m.y. A date older than 10 m.y. (10 - 15 m.y.a.) for this common ancestor is much less probable.

4. The anatomical, biomolecular and fossil data suggest it is highly probable that this last ape-human common ancestor lived in Africa. It is much less probable (but far from impossible) that it evolved somewhere in Eurasia and migrated into Africa.

5. The Dryopiths of the early Miocene (Proconsul species) were similar enough to modern great apes dentally and unspecialized enough postcranially for one or more of them

to be distant ancestral candidates for the living great apes and humans.

6. The Ramapiths most likely are derived from one or more of the early Miocene Dryopiths of Africa.

7. Some of the South Asian Ramapiths (one of the Sivapithecus lineages) probably gave rise to Pongo.

8. Dental similarities make one of the African Ramapiths (such as Kenyapithecus) a possible ancestral candidate for the first hominids, the Australopithecines. Still much more needs to be learned about the Ramapiths in general and, in particular, the African Ramapiths, before their possible hominid ancestry can be confirmed.

One can understand even from this brief survey that the Ramapiths were a diverse group of hominoids. They lived in mixed habitats on three continents and were of many different sizes. Because of this, it has been suggested that the living great apes of the African and Asian rainforests are even more specialized and less diverse than the hominoids that existed in the middle through late Miocene (Pilbeam et al. 1977).

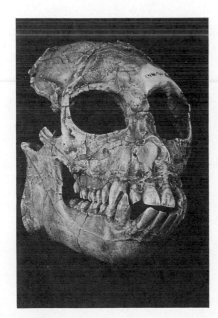

Figure 11.8 P. africanus

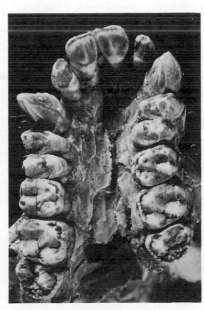

Figure 11.9 P. africanus

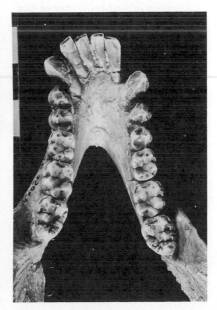

Figure 11.10 P. africanus

145

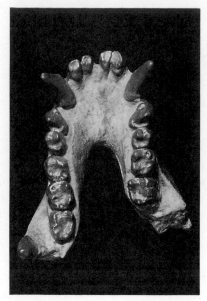 

Figure 11.11 <u>Dryopithecus fontani</u>

Figure 11.12 <u>Sivapithecus indicus</u>

1. This distorted cranium of <u>Proconsul</u> <u>africanus</u> (Figure 11.8) is the only one we have. What features would identify it as a higher primate skull?

2. How is <u>Proconsul</u> less primitive than the skull of <u>Aegyptopithecus</u> of the Oligocene (see Figure 10.2)?

3. Keeping in mind that <u>P.</u> <u>africanus</u> probably weighed about 20 or 30 lbs, does its brain size seem to be about as large relative to body size as that of modern apes?

4.   Using the criteria listed in previous chapters, make a list of the similarities in the teeth and jaws of Proconsul (Figures 11.8, 11.9, 11.10) and of chimpanzees and/or gorillas. Make a second list of all of the differences in the teeth and jaws of the two groups of hominoids.

5.   The Dryopithecus fontani (Figure 11.11) mandible from southern France and other Dryopithecus specimens of Europe are believed to be younger than 17 m.y. Keeping in mind that the orginal Proconsul radiation took place before 22 m.y. in the African forests, does Dryopithecus fontani appear to have possibly been derived from a Proconsul species? Make a list of similarities or dissimilarities of the dentition of the two forms to document your answer.

6.   List the differences between the jaws and teeth of the Sivapiths and those of Proconsul.

7. Compare the face of <u>Sivapithecus indicus</u> (GSP 15000) to those of both a chimpanzee and an orang-utan (Figure 11.5). Which does the fossil most resemble? Make a short list of similarities of GSP 15000 to the living great ape you feel it most resembles, and another list of differences between this fossil specimen and the living great ape it least resembles (chimpanzee or orang-utan).

8. Is the dental pattern of <u>Gigantopithecus</u> similar to that of other Siva-pith specimens? Explain.

10. Draw out your own "solution" to the puzzle of Miocene hominoid evolution and especially the nature of the last common ancestor of apes and humans. Of course a definitive solution is not possible at this time, but by using the disparate pieces of the puzzle we have given, you can make educated guesses of the appearance of the missing pieces.

Chapter 12

Plio-Pleistocene Hominid Evolution

INTRODUCTION

We will now leave the apes to concentrate on undoubted members of our own biological family, referred to as the Pliocene (5.5 to 1.9 m.y.a.) - Pleistocene (1.9 million to 10,000 years before the present) hominids. These are considered hominids primarily because of their obvious adaptations to bipedal locomotion, and because of dental morphologies which emphasized a reduction in the size of the anterior teeth (especially the canines), and a relative increase in the size of the cheek teeth.

The most ancient of the hominids for which we have a good sample of fossils (more than single teeth and jaw fragments) are just under 4 million years old. From this point in time we can follow the broad outlines of our physical evolution to the present day. These are classified in the genus Australopithe-cus, are concentrated in eastern and southern Africa, and are associated with the savannah habitats that characterize these areas of Africa today. The most recent of the australopiths disappears from the fossil record shortly after one million years ago.

Interpretations of the Plio-Pleistocene hominid fossils are fraught with controversies. These controversies, even though contested just as strongly in the scientific literature as are those of the Miocene, are not as critical to the understanding of the broad course of hominid evolution dating from 4 million years ago. The fossil record of this shorter time period is much more complete than that of similar time periods of the Miocene; the broad picture of our physical evolution for this period is quite clear.

In our review we will begin with the most ancient representatives of the australopiths, found at Hadar (Afar), Ethiopia, and Laetoli, Tanzania.

Discoveries of australopiths at Laetoli and Hadar, including the famous "Lucy," (Figure 12.1) were made in the 1970s. These sites are dated by radiometric techniques at between 3 and 4 m.y.a., making these the oldest australopiths to date for which we have good samples. In 1979, Don Johanson, who co-led fossil hunting expeditions to Hadar, and Tim White, who worked at Laetoli with Mary Leakey, described what they considered the unique characteristics of the hominids of these two sites and classified them as a separate species: Australopithecus afarensis (Johanson and White 1979). They described A. afarensis as a good ancestral candidate for not only later australopiths, but for the first species of the genus Homo as well.

These interpretations of the hominid fossils of Hadar and Laetoli are in dispute. Some do not believe that these hominids are morphologically distinct enough to be classified in a separate species and propose instead to put them with the taxon described previously: A. africanus. Others believe that there might be two species of medium-sized and large hominids represented by these fossils (Olson 1981, Falk and Conroy 1983, and Falk 1986). Johanson and White argue that these fossils represent one highly sexually dimorphic species.

We will follow Johanson and White's interpretation while admitting that there is still room for debate, especially with regard to the possibility of two species of australopiths in the fossil assemblage of Hadar, Ethiopia, at about 3 million years ago.

BIPEDALISM

Obviously, bipedalism is one of the most important events in human evolution. We have not yet discovered the selective forces and/or historical accidents that led to

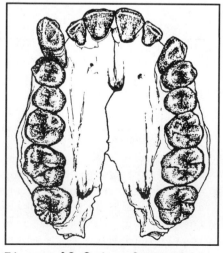

Figure 12.1 A. afarensis
(courtesy, Waveland Press)

Figure 12.2 A. afarensis
(courtesy, Waveland Press)

the origins of bipedalism in
hominids, nor do we know whether
the A. afarensis specimens of
just under 4 m.y. of age represent the beginnings of bipedalism
in primates. Australopithecus
afarensis did, however, possess
all of the morphological characteristics necessary for bipedalism.

However, as we have seen, agility
in the trees is an advantage most
primates possess, and there is no
evidence to suggest that bipedalism precluded at least some use
of the trees. Australopithecus
afarensis possessed curved and
long phalanges relative to later
hominids, and these are characteristics common to extant arboreal primates. The evidence suggests that the australopiths,
while moving bipedally on the
ground, still probably slept in
and took a portion of their diet
from the trees.

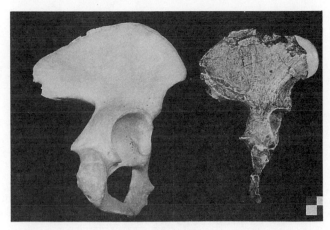

Figure 12.3 Innominata
   Modern Human (left),
   A. africanus (right)

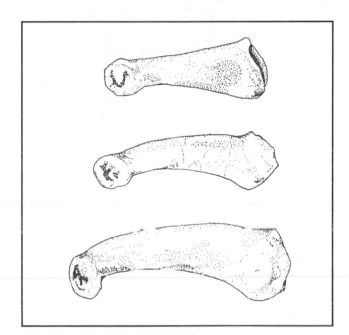

Figure 12.4 Pedal Phalanges
   Modern Human (top),
   A. afarensis (center)
   Chimpanzee (bottom)
   (courtesy, R. Susman)

153

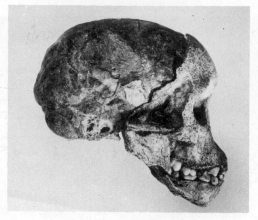

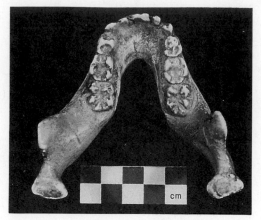

Figure 12.5 <u>A</u>. <u>africanus</u>:
From the Taung Site,
(courtesy, P. Tobias)

Figure 12.6 <u>A</u>. <u>africanus</u>:
Taung

THE SOUTH AFRICAN AUSTRALOPITHS

Because of the lack of volcanic activity in South Africa, it is impossible to attach absolute radiometric dates to these southern sites. In the past decade, however, several have compared the fauna (the antelope, and pigs, for example) associated with the South African australopiths with the fauna of East African fossil sites, most of which do have good absolute radiometric dates. This faunal association has provided reliable relative dates to all but the Taung site (which is a mine site, and has therefore been destroyed; see Dart 1925) and has cleared up some of the confusion concerning the relation- ships of the two South African australopithecines. The approximate ages of the <u>South African australopith fossil sites are listed below</u>:

Kromdraai	1 m.y.a.	<u>Australopithecus</u> <u>robustus</u>
Swartkrans	1 m.y.a.	<u>Australopithecus</u> <u>robustus</u>
Taung	?	<u>Australopithecus</u> <u>africanus</u>
Makapansgat	2 m.y.a.	<u>Australopithecus</u> <u>africanus</u>
Sterkfontein	2.5 m.y.a.	<u>Australopithecus</u> <u>africanus</u>

If based on the South African evidence alone, it would appear that the medium- sized (4 to 5 ft tall, 60 to over 100 lb) <u>A</u>. <u>africanus</u> gave rise to the more recent and slightly larger <u>A</u>. <u>robustus</u>. This view, however, may have to be modified in light of recent discoveries in East Africa.

EAST AFRICAN AUSTRALOPITHS

There is some debate as to whether <u>Australopithecus</u> <u>africanus</u> is represented in the hominid fossils of East Africa (White et al. 1983). Many of the jaw and tooth fragments attributed to <u>A</u>. <u>africanus</u> could be representatives of the first recognized member of the genus <u>Homo</u> (<u>H</u>. <u>habilis</u>). In addition, a cranium from East Turkana (KNM-ER 1813) attributed to the <u>Homo</u> <u>habilis</u> has a cranial capacity below the range of <u>Homo habilis</u> but within the range of <u>A. africanus</u> (Leakey and Walker 1980). As there are no known major geographical or ecological barriers between South and East Africa, there is no reason why <u>A. africanus</u> could not have lived in both areas.

<u>There is no doubt, however, that a large robust species, called A. boisei, lived in East Africa from around 2.5 m.y.a. to just after 1 m.y.a.</u>. <u>A. boisei</u> is found in Olduvai, East Turkana, Omo and a few other East African fossil sites. It is very similar to <u>A. robustus</u> of South Africa, leading many to believe that they should be classified in the same species. In any case, the <u>A. robustus/A. boisei</u> populations represent the culmination of dental trends first observed in some of the Miocene sivapiths, including reduction of the anterior teeth, enlargement of the cheek teeth, and thickening of the jaws. These robust, megadont (large teeth) australopithecines have been called "nutcrackers", and quite possibly nuts were a part of their diet; the large premolars and molars with thick enamel may have provided the surface area for grinding small, tough food objects (e.g. seeds) which needed little slicing and cutting by the small incisors and canines.

These small bipeds with somewhat ape-like upper bodies were very successful for at least 3 million years, but they disappeared from the fossil record soon after 1 million years ago. The cause of their extinction is unknown, but it is possibly related to the expansion in the savanna habitats of their descendants: populations of species of the genus <u>Homo</u>.

A. robustus / A. boisei became extinct just after 1 m.y.a. possibly by the extension of habitat by the genus: Homo.

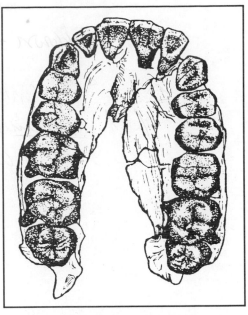

Figure 12.7 <u>A. africanus</u> (courtesy, Waveland Press)

Figure 12.8 <u>A. africanus</u>, (left), <u>A. robustus</u> (right)

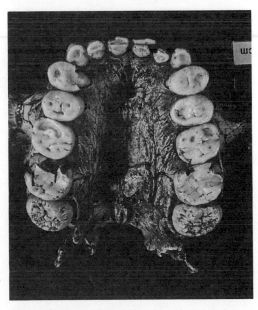

Figure 12.9 <u>A. boisei</u>

- Saw skull from Piltdown → read about it

A. africanus - Steikfontein, South Africa
- hip bone of A. Africanus discovered at Steikfontein in 1947
(what features make it look more like a piped? not like a
biped?

A. boisei → East Africa by Mary Leaky in 1959 @ Olduvai Gorge
(pp. 392-393 in text)

- all other material is from Swartrans - in S. Africa - classified as
A. robustus

- how does robust dentition compare to gracile?
- is hip bone consistent w̄ bipedality?

Homo Habilis : - KNM - 1470 - found East lake Turkana in 1972
        (pp. 439-441 in text)   1.8 my BP
        Geographic Location: Koobi Fora, East Turkana, Kenya
- showed all the features of Homo habilis that were only weakly revealed in
other habiline specimens recovered from Olduvai Gorge
        - endocranial volume: 775 cc
        - weakly developed muscle attachment sites
        - moderate postorbital constriction
        - lightly constructed, globular vault

1. Using the criteria of ape and human dentition from previous chapters, analyze the dentition of <u>A. afarensis</u> (Figure 12.2). In what ways is the dentition ape-like? In what ways is it human-like?

2. Based on these criteria, would you consider <u>A afarensis</u> a hominid? The dentition of what Miocene hominoids resemble <u>A. afarensis</u>?

   Miocene Sivapiths

3. Compare the innominate of <u>A. afarensis</u> ("Lucy") (Figure 12.1) to that of apes and humans. If the innominate of <u>A. afarensis</u> is unavailable, that of the more recent <u>A. africanus</u> will suffice, as it is nearly identical (Figure 12.3). How is it ape-like? How is it human-like? How is it unlike either apes or humans?

4.   Based on the morphology of the innominate, do you believe <u>A.</u> <u>afarensis</u> was bipedal?

5.   Compare the phalanges of <u>A.</u> <u>afarensis</u> (Figure 12.4) to those of apes and humans. How are they ape-like? How are they human-like?

6.   What are the advantages of bipedalism in an open habitat? What are the advantages of an arboreal existence? What are the advantages of combining the utilization of both habitats?

7.   Observe the dentition of the Taung child (Figures 12.5 and 12.6). All but the molars (one in each quadrant) are deciduous. The first permanent molar erupts at about six years of age in modern humans, and at about age 3 in chimpanzees (Schultz 1935). How old do you think the Taung child was at death? Why?

8. Compare the dentition of A. africanus (Figure 12.7) with that of the more ancient A. afarensis (Figure 12.2). In what ways can the dentition of A. afarensis be said to be more primitive than that of A. africanus? Based on this evidence, do you believe A. afarensis is a good ancestral candidate for A. africanus?

9. List the differences between the crania of A. africanus and the more recent A. robustus (Figure 12.8).

10. What are the differences between A. africanus (Figure 12.7) and A. boisei (Figure 12.9) in dental morphology?

11. This exercise is designed to give the student an idea of the reduction in the importance of the anterior teeth and increase in importance of the cheek teeth in the australopiths. Measure the canine at roughly the same level as the molar, and fill in the chart as indicated.

	Canine Area Length X Width	First Molar Area	C/M
Pan			
Gorilla			
Pongo			
A. afarensis			
A. africanus			
A. robustus			
A. boisei			
Homo sapiens			

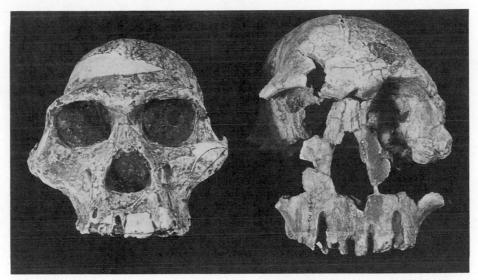

Figure 12.10 <u>A.</u> <u>africanus</u> (left), <u>H.</u> <u>habilis</u> (right)

HOMO HABILIS

A few fossil fragments discovered in South
Africa probably represent an early <u>Homo</u> species contemporaneous with <u>A.</u> <u>robustus</u> at 2
m.y.a., but the existence of early <u>Homo</u> was
not confirmed until specimens began to show
up in East African sites. In the early
1960s at Olduvai Gorge, Louis Leakey found a
mandible with most of the adult dentition and
a few skull fragments which he and his colleagues classified as <u>Homo</u> <u>habilis</u>, or
"handy-man" (Leakey et al. 1964). Since the
early 1970s, Richard Leakey has uncovered
more complete specimens of <u>H.</u> <u>habilis</u> at East
Turkana (Leakey 1974) (see also Figures 12.10
and 12.11).

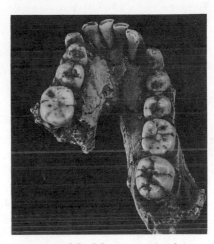

Figure 12.11 <u>H.</u> <u>habilis</u>
Mandible

Postcranial remains of this hominid are
still quite rare, but a recent discovery by
Johanson and others (1987) indicates that <u>H.</u>
<u>habilis</u> at 1.8 m.y.a. was only slightly lar-
ger than the much more ancient "Lucy" (A.L.
288-1, Figure 12.1), which was only about 3.5
feet tall. Even though this <u>Homo</u> <u>habilis</u>
specimen (OH 62) was still quite primitive in
some ways (for example the forelimbs are
still quite long relative to its hindlimbs),
most of a foot (OH 8) found at Olduvai Gorge
and attributed to <u>H.</u> <u>habilis</u> suggests that
they were at least partially bipedal. More
complete ground-living and bipedal adaptations apparently evolved quite rapidly after
this, as indicated by a juvenile <u>H.</u> <u>erectus</u>
specimen, dated at 1.6 m.y.a. (Brown et al.

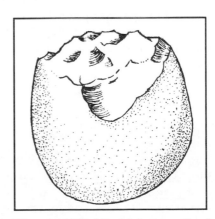

Figure 12.12 Oldowan Tool

161

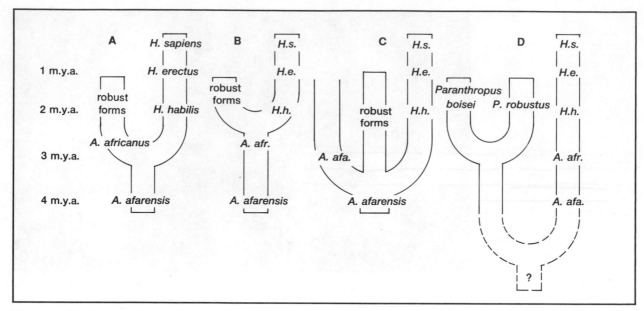

Figure 12.13 Phylogenetic Hypotheses of Plio-Pleistocene Hominid Evolution
Johanson and White (1979) Favor Hypothesis A

1985), which clearly demonstrates these adaptations.

Johanson and White (1979) believe that A. afarensis is a good ancestral candidate for not only later australopiths but also for Homo habilis, while others believe that A. africanus is the better candidate (Figure 12.13). The Johanson and White phylogeny will have to be modified, however, in light of a recent discovery of a robust australopithecine from Kenya, dated at 2.5 m.y.a.. This hominid, which is probably A. boisei (Walker et al. 1986), is about one-half million years older than previously known robust australopithecine specimens. Further evidence suggests that these robust hominids are among the fossil assemblage at Hadar, Ethiopia, at 3 m.y.a. and that there are, therefore, two lineages of Australopithecus at that site (as discussed before).

H. habilis is now thought to have been the first hominid to use the Oldowan tools (Figure 12.12) found at several sites. These tools were used to butcher the large animals scavenged (and possibly hunted) by these hominids. Traditional interpretations of archeological evidence have also suggested that H. habilis occupied home bases and shared food in a manner similar to living hunters and gatherers, but these interepretations have been challenged. The social patterns of these early hominids are still, therefore, not well-understood.

HOMO ERECTUS

Regardless of which phylogenetic hypothesis concerning the ancestors of H. habilis is ultimately correct, the sequence of species thorugh the lineage of Homo seems clear: Homo habilis gave rise to H. erectus at around 1.5 m.y.a., which in turn gave rise to archaic H. sapiens at around 0.3 m.y.a..

The Homo erectus (Figures 12.14, 12.15, 12.16, 12.17) stage of human evolution lasted more than a million years (1.6 to 0.3 m.y.a.). The earliest fossils of

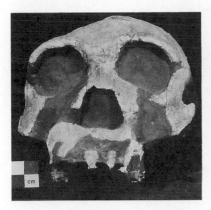

Figure 12.14 <u>H. erectus</u>
KNM-ER 3733

Figure 12.15 <u>H. erectus</u>
KNM-ER 3733

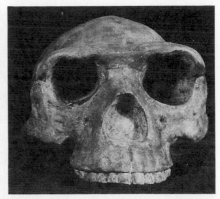

Figure 12.16 <u>H. erectus</u>
<u>pekinensis</u>

this species are found in East Africa at
East Turkana and Olduvai Gorge, but sometime
after 1 million years ago, populations of <u>H.</u>
<u>erectus</u> migrated out of Africa into temperate
and tropical regions of Eurasia. That they
were able to live in these colder climates is
a tribute to their behavioral plasticity
and increasing cultural complexity.

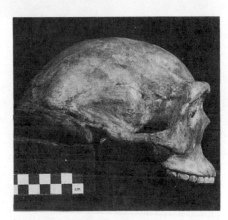

Figure 12.17 <u>H. erectus</u>
<u>pekinensis</u>

A new tool type, the Acheulian hand axe (Figure 12.16), appears with the fossil remains
of early <u>H. erectus</u> in East Africa. The
Acheulian stone tools are found in parts of
Africa, western Europe, and western India,
but in eastern Europe and East Asia a different type of stone tool sometimes referred to as "chopper-tools" are found associated with <u>H. erectus</u> remains.

As with previous fossil species it is difficult to reconstruct the social behavior of
<u>Homo erectus</u>. In the past, there was a
tendency to project the social characteristics of modern human hunter and gatherer
population back to <u>H. erectus</u> and other fossil hominid species. Today, however, some
archaeologists and paleoanthropologists question the hunting capabilities of <u>H. erectus</u>
and later archaic <u>H. sapiens</u> (e.g. Binford,
1984). They must at least have hunted animals smaller than themselves as do living
chimpanzees and baboons, and archaeological
remains leave little doubt that they ate
animals almost as large or larger than
themselves. Whether they hunted or scavenged these larger animals, however, is a

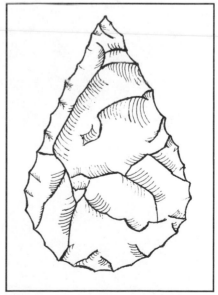

Figure 12.18 Acheulean
Hand Axe

Figure 12.19 Steinheim, probably transitional between <u>H. erectus</u> and <u>H. sapiens</u>, from Germany

Figure 12.20 Steinheim

subject of debate.

<u>H. erectus</u> populations must have resembled living hunters and gatherers in some respects, however. Archaeological data of younger populations of <u>H. erectus</u>, such as those of Zhoukoudian, China and Terra Amata, France, (both more recent than 0.5 m.y.a.), show that they used fire, lived in home bases or temporary camps, built temporary living shelters, and relied on gathering and hunting for subsistence.

ARCHAIC <u>HOMO SAPIENS</u>

Fossil hominids from Europe dated at around 0.3 to 0.2 m.y.a. show more <u>sapiens</u>-like characteristics while retaining a few <u>erectus</u>-like traits. These hominids were apparently making the transition from the <u>Homo erectus</u> stage to an early form of our own species (Figures 12.19 and 12.20). The classic Neandertals of Europe and the Near East are the most well-known populations of archaic <u>H. sapiens</u>. Neandertals lived during most of the last glacial (Würm) period, from just over 100,000 years ago until they were replaced by populations of modern <u>H. sapiens</u> about 30,000 years ago.

One of the major trends in the evolution of the <u>Homo</u> lineage continued in Neandertal specimens, that of greater encephalization, or larger brains. In fact, some of these hominids have larger cranial capacities than do most modern humans! The cranium (Figure 12.21) of a Neandertal is lower and longer than those of modern <u>Homo sapiens</u>. The teeth and jaws, while a bit smaller on the average than those of their predecessors, are quite large relative to modern humans, so the lower face still retains a prognathic appearance. Observe the base of the cranium of a classic Neandertal and that of a modern <u>Homo sapiens</u>. The flatness of this area just behind the palate of the Neandertal is interpreted by some as evidence that they did not have vocal tracts that were as long as those of modern humans and that, therefore, they could not articulate as wide an array of sounds. Postcranially, Neandertals were shorter than modern humans, but extremely robust.

The Neandertal cultural remains, collectively termed the Mousterian culture, were more complex and varied than those associated with H. erectus populations. More than 60 different types of scrapers, knives, points, burins and other stone tools have been identified in Neandertal cultural assemblages (Figure 12.22). Probable spear points associated with Neandertal remains are the first points to appear in the archeological record.

That later populations of archaic H. sapiens sometimes buried their dead is further evidence of their increased cultural complexity from that of earlier hominids. Over a dozen Neandertal burials have been discovered in Europe and the Near East, though the significance of these burials is still debated. These and other cultural artifacts, however, indicate that they lived much like living hunters and gatherers. This is in sharp contrast to the picture of Neandertals painted by paleontologists and anthropologists of the early part of this century, who incorrectly emphasized the "ape-like" and brutish characteristics of these people; a picture that unfortunately still persists among some segments of the public today.

MODERN HOMO SAPIENS

Modern Homo sapiens occur in fossil records dated at between 30,000 and 40,000 years before the present. Modern specimens of this age have been found in

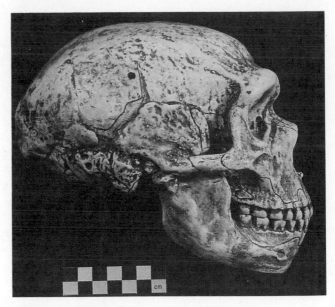

Figure 12.21 Archaic Homo sapiens (Neandertal): La Chapelle-aux-Saints

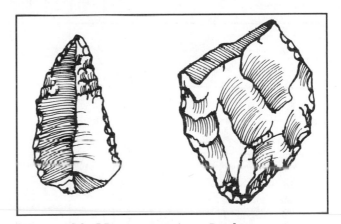

Figure 12.22 Mousterian Tools

Figure 12.23 Skhūl V

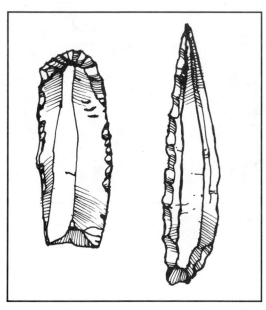

Figure 12.24 Blade Tools

South Africa, later in Europe, and from about 10,000 years ago throughout the Old World, New World, and Australia. As expected, some fossil specimens from the early part of this period show characteristics common to both archaic and modern Homo sapiens, and are believed to be transitional fossils. The Skhūl V cranium from Mount Carmel, Israel, dated at about 35,000 years before the present, is a classic transitional specimen (Figure 12.23).

The interpretation of the beginnings of Homo sapiens is not without controversy, however. Two theories, corresponding to the current paradigm debate between advocates of gradualism and punctuated equilibrium (see Chapter 4), attempt to explain the disappearance of the Neandertals from Europe. Those who argue for the gradualism theory believe that archaic populations, wherever they existed, gradually evolved into the modern forms. On the other hand, the punctuated equilibrium theorists state that modern Homo sapiens evolved in one area, possibly Africa or West Asia, migrated to Europe and other areas of the Old World, and replaced archaic populations, either by genocide or by competition for resources. Though insufficient data exist to answer this question, there is little doubt that modern Homo sapiens evolved in some way from archaic populations.

With the appearance of the completely modern morphology of Homo sapiens came the capability of fully articulate speech. Some linguists and anatomists argue, on the basis of certain features of the bases of the crania of fossil species, that the more ancient forms had no speech, or that they could not articulate many vowels (Lieberman and Crelin 1971). This argument is supported to some extent by the relatively slow pace of cultural evolution as measured by stone tool technology from 2 m.y.a. until the appearance of modern humans, as it can be argued that speech can hasten cultural evolution. On the other hand, the Neandertals, as discussed above, exhibited significant

166

cultural complexity and such distinctive human behavior patterns as burying their dead. It is hard to believe, therefore, that the Neandertals did not have some sort of fairly complex communication capabilities.

There can be no question, however, that with the appearance of modern _Homo sapiens_ there began a cultural "explosion" that continues and gains momentum through the present day. Upper Paleolithic hominids of Europe between 25,000 and 12,000 years ago, for example, made blade stone tools (Figure 12.24). This is a much more efficient way of using the available stone in that significantly more cutting edge and many more varieties of tool can be created per pound of stone. The first musical instruments in the archeological record are found in Upper Paleolithic cultural remains, as well as the first needles, jewlery, spear throwers (atlatls), harpoons, and evidence of the first bows and arrows. The magnificent cave paintings of France and Spain are also associated with this period.

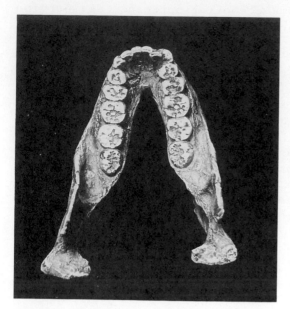

Figure 12.25 Unknown Mandible for Exercise 2

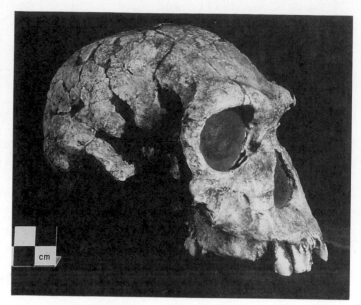

Figure 12.26 Unknown Cranium for Exercise 3

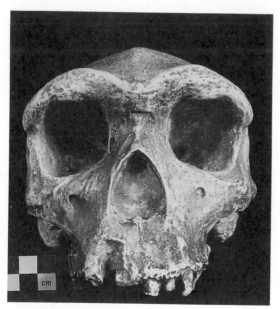

Figure 12.27 Unknown Cranium for Exercise 4

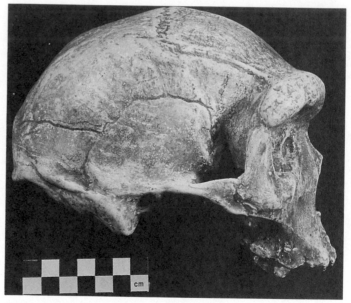

Figure 12.28 Unknown Cranium for Exercise 4

<u>Exercises</u>

1. Compare the OH 7 mandible of <u>Homo</u> <u>habilis</u> (Figure 12.11) to the jaws of the species of the Australopiths (Figures 12.2, 12.6, 12.7, and 12.9). Which species of Australopith does OH 7 most resemble? How does the dentition differ?

2. Compare the mandible pictured in Figure 12.25 to those of other hominids discussed in this chapter. Based especially on the relative size of the cheek teeth to anterior teeth and the shape of the dental arcade, how would you classify this unknown?

3. Compare the cranium pictured in Figure 12.26 to those of other hominids discussed in this chapter. How would you classify this unknown?

4. Compare the cranium pictured in Figures 12.27 and 12.28 to those of other hominids discussed in this chapter. How would you classify this unknown?

5. Is A. afarensis or A. africanus a better ancestral candidate for H. habilis? Why?

6. Make a list of the differences between Homo erectus and archaic Homo sapiens crania.

7. In which species discussed in this chapter do you first notice a chin?

8. What are the characteristics of Steinheim (Figures 12.19 and 12.20) which would make it transitional between Homo erectus and Homo sapiens? Tattersal (1986) and others believe that archaic Homo sapiens, including the Steinheim specimen, will be divided into several species in the future. Do you agree with this claim?

9. If you have casts of Neandertal postcranial remains, compare them to the postcrania of modern humans. What was the relative stature of Neandertal? The relative robusticity? Aside from size differences, are there marked differences in morphology between the two forms?

10. What characteristics would lead you to believe that Skhūl V (Figure 12.23) is transitional between archaic and modern Homo sapiens?

11. In what morphological characteristics are the Neandertals different from modern <u>Homo</u> <u>sapiens</u>?

BIBLIOGRAPHY

Andrews, P. J.
    1983   "The Natural History of <u>Sivapithecus</u>." In: <u>New Interpretations of Ape and Human Ancestry</u>, R. Ciochon and R. Corruccini (eds.), New York: Plenum Press, pp. 441-463.

Bass, W. M.
    1987   <u>Human Osteology: A Laboratory and Field Manual</u> (3rd Ed.). Columbia, Mo.: Missouri Archaeological Society Special Publication No. 2.

Binford, L. R.
    1984   <u>Faunal Remains from Klasies River Mouth</u>. Orlando, FLA.: Academic Press.

Brooks, S. T.
    1985   Personal Communication

_____

    1986   "Comments on 'Known' Age at Death Series." Presented in conjunction with "Skeletal Age Standards Derived from an Extensive Multi-Racial Sample of Modern Americans," by J. Suchey and D. Katz, at the Fifty-Fifth Annual Meeting of the American Association of Physical Anthropologists, Albuquerque, New Mexico.

Brown, F., J. Harris, R. Leakey and A. Walker
    1985   "Early <u>Homo erectus</u> Skeleton from West Lake Turkana, Kenya." <u>Nature</u>, 316:788-792.

Brues, A. M.
    1977   <u>People and Races</u>. New York: MacMillan Publishing Company, Inc.

Campbell, B.G.
    1976   <u>Human Evolution: An Introduction to Man's Adaptations</u> (2nd Ed.). New York: Aldine Publishing Company.

_____

    1985   <u>Human Evolution: An Introduction to Man's Adaptations</u> (3rd Ed.). New York: Aldine Publishing Company.

Ciochon, R. L.
1983   "Hominoid Cladistics and the Ancestry of Modern Apes and Humans." In: <u>New Interpretations of Ape and Human Ancestory</u>, R. Chiochon and R. Corruccini (eds.), New York: Plenum Press, pp. 783-843.

Ciochon, R. L. and A. B. Chiarelli (eds.)
1980   <u>Evolutionary Biology of the New World Monkeys and Continental Drift</u>. New York: Plenum Press.

Ciochon, R. L., D. E. Savage, T. Tint, and B. Maw
1985   "Anthropoid Origins in Asia? New Discoveries of <u>Amphipithecus</u> from the Eocene of Burma." <u>Science</u>, 229:756-759.

Clark, W.E. Le Gros
1959   <u>The Antecedents of Man</u>. New York: Harper and Row Publishers.

Cronin, J. E.
1983   "Apes, Humans, and Molecular Clocks. A Reappraisal." In: <u>New Interpretations of Apes and Human Ancestry</u>, R. Ciochon and R. Corruccini (eds.), New York: Plenum Press, pp. 115-150.

Dart, R.
1925   "<u>Australopithecus africanus</u>: The Man Ape of South Africa." <u>Nature</u>, 115:195-199.

Eldredge, N. and S. J. Gould
1972   "Punctuated Equilibria: An Alternative to Phyletic Gradualism." In: <u>Models in Paleobiology</u>, T. J. M. Schopf (ed.), San Francisco: Freeman, Cooper and Co., pp. 82-115.

Falk, D.
1986   "Evolution of Cranial Blood Drainage in Hominids: Enlarged Occipital/Margina Sinuses and Emissary Foramina." <u>American Journal of Physical Anthropology</u>, 70:311-324.

Falk, D. and G. C. Conroy
1983   "The Cranial Venous Sinus System in <u>Australopithecus afarensis</u>." <u>Nature</u>, 306:779-781.

Fleagle, J. G.
1976   "Locomotion and Posture of the Malayan Siamang and Implications for Hominoid Evolution." <u>Folia Primatologica</u>, 26:245-269.

Fleagle, J. C. and R. F. Kay
1983   "New Interpretations of the Phyletic Position of Oligocene Hominoids." In: <u>New Interpretations of Apes and Human Ancestry</u>, R. Ciochon and R. Corruccini (eds.), New York: Plenum Press, pp. 181-210.

Fleagle, J. C. and E. L. Simons
1978   "Humeral Morphology of the Earliest Apes." <u>Nature</u>, 276:705-706.

France, D.L.
1983   <u>Sexual Dimorphism in the Human Humerus</u>. Unpublished Ph.D. Dissertation, University of Colorado, Boulder.

Gardner, E. J.
 1975   *Principles of Genetics* (5th Ed.).   New York: John Wiley & Sons,
         Inc.

Gingerich, P. D.
 1984   "Primate Evolution: Evidence From the Fossil Record, Comparative
         Morphology,   and   Molecular   Biology." *Yearbook of Physical*
         Anthropology, 27:57-72.

Goodman, M., M. L. Baba and L.C. Darga
 1983   "The Bearing of Molecular Data on the Cladogenesis and Times of
         Divergence of Hominoid Lineages."   In: *New Interpretations of*
         Apes and Human Ancestry, R. L. Ciochon and R. S. Corruccini
         (eds.), New York: Plenum Press, pp. 67-86.

Gould, S. J. and N. Eldridge
 1977   "Punctuated Equilibria: the Tempo and Mode of Evolution Reconsi-
         dered." *Paleobiology*, 3:115-151.

Greenfield, L. O.
 1979   "On the Adaptive Pattern of *Ramapithecus*." *American Journal of*
         Physical Anthropology, 50:527-548.

Johanson, D. C. and T. D. White
 1979   "A Systematic Assessment of Early African Hominids."   *Science*,
         203:321-330.

Johanson, D., F. Masao, G. Eck, T. White, R. Walter, W. Kimbel, B. Asfaw, P.
Manega, P. Ndessokia, and G. Suwa
 1987   "New Partial Skeleton of *Homo habilis* from Olduvai Gorge, Tan-
         zania." *Nature*, 327: 205-209.

Katz, D., and J. M. Suchey
 1986   "Age Determination of the Male Os Pubis." *American Journal of*
         Physical Anthropology, 69:427-435.

Kay, R. F. and E. L. Simons
 1983   "A Reassessment of the Relationship Between Later Miocene and
         Subsequent Hominoidea." In: *New Interpretations of Ape and Human*
         Ancestry, R. Ciochon and R. Corruccini (eds.), New York: Plenum
         Press, pp. 577-624.

King, M. C. and A. C. Wilson
 1975   "Evolution at Two Levels in Human and Chimpanzees." *Science*,
         188:107-116.

Kitchin, F. D., W. H. Evans, C. A. Clarke, R. B. McConnel, and P. M. Sheppard
 1959   "PTC Taste Response and Thyroid Disease." *British Medical Journal*,
         1:1069-1074.

Krogman, W. M.
 1939   "A Guide to the Identification of Human Skeletal Material."   *FBI*
         Law Enforcement Bulletin, 8(8): 3-31.

1962   The Human Skeleton in Forensic Medicine. Springfield: C. C Thomas.

Lartet, E.
   1856   "Note Sur la Decouverte Recent d'un Machoire de Singes Supe-
               rieurs." Compte Rendus de l'Academie de Sciences (Paris), 43.

Leakey, L. S. B., P. V. Tobias and J. R. Napier
   1964   "A New Species of the Genus Homo from Olduvai Gorge."   Nature,
               202:7-9.

Leakey, R. E. F.
   1974   "Fvidence of Lower Pleistocene Hominids from East Rudolf, Kenya,
               1973." Nature, 248:653-656.

Leakey, R. E. F. and A. C. Walker
   1980   "On the Status of Australopithecus afarensis." Science, 207:1103.

Lieberman, P. and E. S. Crelin
   1971   "On the Speech of Neanderthal." Linguistic Inquiry, 2:201-222.

Maderson, P. F. A., R. P. Alberch, B. C. Goodwin, S. J. Gould, A. Hoffman,
J. D. Murray, D. M. Raup, A. de Ricgles, A. Seilacher, G. P. Wagner, and D. B.
Wake.
   1982   "The Role of Development in Macroevolutionary Change: Group
               Report."   In: Evolution and Development, J. T. Bonner (ed.),
               Berlin: Dahlem Konferenzen, Spinger-Verlag, pp. 279-312.

Martin, R. and K. Saller
   1957   Lehrbuch der Anthropologie, Stuttgart: Gustav Fischer Verlag.

Mayr, E.
   1970   Populations, Species and Evolution. Cambridge: Harvard University
               Press.

   1981   "Biological   Classification: Toward a Synthesis of Opposing
               Methodologies." Science, 214:510-516.

McKern, T. W., and T. D. Stewart
   1957   "Skeletal Age Changes in Young American Males, Technical Report
               EP-45." Natick, MA: U.S. Army Quartermaster Research and
               Development Center.

Meindl, R. S. and C. O. Lovejoy
   1985   "Ectocranial Suture Closure: A Revised Method for the Determina-
               tion of Skeletal Age at Death Based on the Lateral-Anterior Su-
               tures." American Journal of Physical Anthropology, 68: 57-66.

Montague, M. F. Ashley
   1960   Introduction to Physical Anthropology. Springfield: C. C Thomas.

Mourant, A. E.
   1954   The Distribution of the Human Blood Groups. Oxford: Blackwell.

Mourant, A. E., A. C. Kopec, and K. Domaniewska-Sobczak
   1958   The ABO Blood Groups. Springfield: C.C Thomas.

Olson, T. R.
   1981   "Basicranial Morphology of Extant Hominoids and Pliocene Hominids: The New Material from the Hadar Formation, Ethiopia and Its Significance in Early Human Evolution and Taxonomy." In: Aspects of Human Evolution, C. B. Stringer (ed.), London: Taylor and Francis, pp. 99-128.

Olson, S. L. and D. T. Rasmusson
   1986   "Paleoenvironment of the Earliest Hominoids: New Evidence from the Oligocene Avi of Egypt." Science, 233:1202-1204.

Phenice, T. W.
   1969   "A Newly Developed Visual Method of Sexing the Os Pubis." American Journal of Physical Anthropology, 30:297-302.

Pickford, M.
   1983   "Sequence and Environments of the Lower and Middle Miocene Hominoids of Western Kenya." In: New Interpretations of Ape and Human Ancestry, R. Ciochon and R. Corruccini (eds.), New York: Plenum Press, pp. 421-439.

Pilbeam, D.
   1984   "The Descent of Hominoids and Hominids." Scientific American, 250:84-96.

Pilbeam, D. R., G. Meyer, G. Badgley, M. Rose, M. Pickford, A. Behrensmeyer and S. M. Ibrahim Shah.
   1977   "New Hominoid Primates from the Siwaliks of Pakistan and Their Bearing on Hominoid Evolution." Nature, 270:689-695.

Roff, R. A. and I. C. Kaufman
   1983   Embryos, Genes and Evolution. New York: Macmillan.

Ruzu, S.M., J. C. Barry, D. Pilbeam, M. D. Rose, S. M. Ibrahim Shuh, and S. Ward
   1983   "New Hominoid Primates from the Middle Miocene Chinji Formation, Potwar Plateau, Pakistan." Nature, 306:52-54.

Rose, M. D.
   1983   "Miocene Hominoid Postcranial Morphology: Monkey-like, Ape-like, Neither or Both?" In: New Interpretations of Ape and Human Ancestry, R. Ciochon and R. Corruccini (eds.), New York: Plenum Press, pp. 405-417.

Sarich, V. M. and A. C. Wilson
   1967   "Immunological Time Scale for Hominid Evolution." Science 158: 1200-1203.

Schultz, A. H.
   1935   "Eruption and Decay of the Permanent Teeth in Primates." American Journal of Physical Anthropology, XIX:489-581.

_____
1937   "Proportions, Variability and Asymmetries of the Long Bones of the Limbs and the Clavicles in Man and Apes." Human Biology 9:281-328.

_____
1973   "The Recent Hominoid Primates." In: The Origin and Evolution of Man: Readings in Physical Anthropology, A. Montagu (ed.)New York: Thomas Y. Crowell Company.

Schwartz, J. H.
  1984   "The Evolutionary Relationships of Man and Orang-utans." Nature, 308:501-505.

Sibley, C. G. and J. E. Ahlquist
  1984   "The Phylogeny of the Hominoid Primates as Indicated by DNA-DNA Hybridization." Journal of Molecular Evolution, 20:2-15.

Simons, E. L. and D. R. Pilbeam
  1965   "Preliminary Revision of the Dryopithecinae (Pongidae, Anthropoidea)." Folia Primatologia, 3:81-152.

Stewart, T. D.
  1979   Essentials of Forensic Anthropology: Especially as Developed in the United States. Springfield: C. C Thomas.

Tattersall, I.
  1986   "Species Recognition in Human Paleontology." Journal of Human Evolution, 15:165-175.

Templeton, A. R.
  1983   "Phylogenetic Inference from Restriction Endonuclease Cleavage Site Maps with Particular Reference to the Evolution of Humans and the Apes." Evolution 37(2):221-224.

_____

  1985   "The Phylogeny of the Hominoid Primates: a Statistical Analysis of the DNA-DNA Hybridization Data." Molecular Biology and Evolution, 2:420-433.

Todd, T. W.
  1920-21 "Age Changes in the Pubic Bone." American Journal of Physical Anthropology, 3:285-334; 4:1-70.

Walker, A. C. and M. Pickford
  1983   "New Postcranial Fossils of Proconsul africanus and Proconsul nyanzae." In: New Interpretations of Ape and Human Ancestry, R. Ciochon and R. Corruccini (eds.), New York: Plenum Press, pp. 325-352.

Walker, A. and R. E. Leakey, J. M. Harris and F. H. Brown
  1986   "2.5-M.yr. Australopithecus boisei from West of Lake Turkana, Kenya." Nature, 322:517-522.

Ward, S. C. and D. R. Pilbeam
    1983   "Maxillofacial Morphology of Miocene Hominoids from Africa and
            Indo-Pakistan." In: New Interpretations of Ape and Human Ances-
            try, R. Ciochon and R. Corruccini (eds.), New York: Plenum Press,
            pp. 211-238.

White, T. D., D. C. Johanson and W. H. Kimbel
    1983   "Australopithecus africanus: Its Phyletic Position Reconsidered."
            In: New Interpretations of Ape and Human Ancestry, R. Ciochon and
            R. Corruccini (eds.), New York: Plenum Press, pp. 721-789.

Index